Now What?

*The Ongoing Pursuit of
Improved Performance*

Now What?

The Ongoing Pursuit of Improved Performance

Dan John

Foreword
Chip Morton

On Target Publications
Santa Cruz, CA

Now What?
The Ongoing Pursuit of Improved Performance

Dan John

Foreword by Chip Morton

Copyright © 2017 Daniel Arthur John
Foreword © 2017 Chip Morton

Graphics: Nick Clark

ISBN-13: 978-1-931046-68-8
First printing March 2017

On Target Publications
P O Box 1335
Aptos, California 95001 USA
otpbooks.com

Library of Congress Cataloging-in-Publication Data

Names: John, Dan, 1957– author.
Title: Now what? : the ongoing pursuit for improved performance / Dan John ; foreword Chip Morton.
Description: Santa Cruz, CA : On Target Publications, 2017.
Identifiers: LCCN 2016053852 | ISBN 9781931046688 (pbk.)
Subjects: LCSH: Athletes--Training of. | Physical fitness. | Physical education and training.
Classification: LCC GV711.5 .J653 2017 | DDC 613.7/11--dc23
LC record available at https://lccn.loc.gov/2016053852

Also by Dan John

Can You Go?

Before We Go

Intervention

Never Let Go

Mass Made Simple

From Dad to Grad

Easy Strength (with Pavel Tsatsouline)

Fat Loss Happens on Monday (with Josh Hillis)

Dedication

To Lonnie Wade

Lonnie was there for my father,
and Lonnie was there for me.

His kindness inspires excellence.

And to the memory of my friends on that
terrible day in August.

Contents

Foreword

I was honored and appreciative when Dan asked me to write the introduction to *Now What? Honored* because I respect Dan's prolific work as a writer, and his ability to coach us all at the same time. I *appreciate* that he asked, because he has helped me see the "give and take" of the coaching process through a different lens. He provides a fresh view, helping to crystallize my thoughts on programming and knitting together training within the fabric of everyday life and all of its demands. Dan's books and articles have impacted how I layer together the various components to build a sound training program, what I look for in a workout, and how I present it to my players. This was the impetus to get to know Dan better, to spend time with him, to exchange ideas and forge a new friendship. His simple and straightforward message has made me a better coach in a profession where success often resides in having good information to share, the ability to teach it clearly, and having the heart to serve others, building good relationships with the people in our care.

Building relationships and intertwining the threads of our goals and training with career, family and community are themes that are woven throughout Dan's work. A living, breathing example of this connection is a fine gentleman I've come to know named Lonnie Wade; Dan has dedicated this book to Lonnie. It turns out that Lonnie's younger son is a Bengals fan and Lonnie had hoped to bring the whole family to Cincinnati to see a game. As Lonnie was sharing his thoughts, Dan mentioned that he had "a friend in Cincinnati" who might be able to help. Dan called me to ask if there was something I could do to enrich this family memory, and I arranged for Lonnie and his family to be our guests at the Saturday walk-through practice the day before the game. It turned out it was *my* pleasure to meet the Wade family. We had a marvelous visit; I was glad to help and thankful I could share in the experience. This was a great example of Dan's care for others, which in this case was made possible through our relationship, having its roots in our conversations about training.

I met Dan John, in person, for the first time at Discus Camp at Denison University, in June of 2011. In discovering his writing earlier that year, I found his words were those of a coach who had actually trained athletes—real people—not just an "expert" providing theoretical ideas that sound good in a workshop, but may not be practical.

Please don't misread this. Dan has done his homework; he's a student of the game; he reads the literature and converses with learned people in the field. But he has also been mentored by wonderful coaches, and his ideas have been tested in the crucible of preparation—getting people to perform at their very best, whether they be athletes, military operators or simply those whose training goal is to gain a fuller, more productive quality of life.

I sought Dan out to dig deeper into his thoughts on training when, after spending most of my adult life making a living as a strength coach, I was about to return to my roots in coaching.

You see, my first coaching assignment when I entered grad school in 1985, was as the strength coach at Franklin Heights High School in Columbus, Ohio. Twenty-six years later, when our oldest son entered high school, I volunteered to run the strength and conditioning program for his high school wrestling team. As expected, Dan's insights proved invaluable in helping me design a training program for a large group of younger athletes with no appreciable training history—I needed realistic programming ideas I could teach to 9th to 12th graders, and their coaches, that could be maintained throughout a rigorous wrestling season. Once again, Dan shared not only ideas on how to structure large group training, but also deeper perspectives on realistic expectations and how to help these athletes set and reach their goals.

Dan's recommendations on planning, programming and performance are effective. More importantly, they are likable, learnable and certainly applicable in real-life settings.

When you review the library of Dan John's work, the titles of his books alone tell his story of community, caring and relationship building.

> ***Never Let Go***—*Exhortation; Think on these things!*
>
> ***Intervention***—*Clarity and care; Getting from point A to point B.*
>
> ***Can You Go?***—*Honesty; What do we work on next?*
>
> ***Before We Go***—*Encouragement; New ideas to inspire.*
>
> ***Now What?***—*Empathy; Here's what we'll do now!*

As I read Dan's work, my goals are two-fold. First, I am a life-long learner, always seeking new ideas I can apply to better serve my athletes and those under my care. Secondly, I enjoy the training process and building my personal practice of movement and strength development. When reading Dan's writing, it always seems like I'm having a conversation because I know his voice and it's familiar (you can, too—there are plenty of interviews online!). Easily the most accessible way to get to know him is by reading his thoughts. Whether with new ideas or a new way to look at old ideas, he teaches us how to plan better, or at least things to consider when making plans and how to prepare more thoroughly—what to look for and what to watch out for.

In *Now What?* Dan presents basic tools and training principles from his experiences as an athlete and coach, and applies them with experienced hands and through empathetic eyes toward the personal growth of his readers. Dan shares insights we can invest in the training lives of our athletes, clients and ourselves—ideas that will fit our professional and private lives…a reasonable approach to help us all reach our goals and bringing greater satisfaction while working through the process.

Pick up this book, join the conversation and be a part the community.

— Chip Morton
Strength and Conditioning Coach
Cincinnati Bengals

Introduction

THERE IS A LIFE EXPERIENCE that is hard to explain to some people. If you haven't yet experienced it, it might be hard to have empathy for this particular feeling. It is a relatively simple thing to ask:

Now what?

For many, it is the morning after the graduation party, when we roll out of bed without any class schedule or place to be...and then notice the diploma and wonder:

Now what?

Don't share this with your partner, but it is a rare spouse who hasn't taken a moment after the wedding ceremony, the honeymoon, and the return of multiple fondue pots who has not wondered:

Now what?

For the athlete, for the performer, there comes a time in every career where the goal has been reached—or not reached—and we need to take a moment to ask:

Now what?

The answer to the question of *Now what?* is action.

But, sometimes we sit in front of a mass of papers, a stuffed inbox, and a pile of dirty clothes and wonder: *Now what?*

I would argue, start the washer first!

The lessons learned about the road to success from elite athletes and performers can make everyone's life better. From de-cluttering the inbox or letter pile with a shark habit, to applying pirate maps to ongoing health and fitness, most people can free up some mental space to focus on moving ahead with all of life's goals and dreams.

Elite performers focus on the fundamentals and basics more thoroughly than the hobbyist. Elite performers keep their heads clear, carving out the clutter of life—both the important and the unimportant—with a scalpel. When needed, the elite focus on two- to twelve-week programs to shore up a weakness or some other issue. Elite performance is principle based.

Most of us can learn from this "carving of the clutter." At times, we can follow a program, but most of the time, we can adopt a simple list of pirate maps for our fitness, health and longevity needs and goals.

The stumbling block of *Now what?* soon takes on a new meaning. After emptying the inbox and finishing the laundry, we can ask *Now what?* as the start of a new adventure, a new challenge.

In this book, I outline a simple quadrant showing how I teach elite performers the tools to deal with life, living and high-end achievement. And if you don't think you're an elite performer, I would like you to reconsider this.

If you work a job, raise kids, help out in the community, rake your leaves, mow your lawn, strive to eat like an adult and still try to train…well, you are elite! Very few people do the simplest of training regimes, like taking a walk, so by simple math, you are elite.

Studying elite performance and the lessons learned from both success and failure can impact every area of your life. True, some people win lotteries, but most people who are successful in the area of finance used basic tools and principles, over time, to get them there.

I always find insight in this quote from Bob Hope, the late, great comedian and movie star: *I've always been in the right place and time. Of course, I steered myself there.*

In the second half of this book, we will look at a simple formula for raising performance, the APE method. Every step, clue and idea in this formula can be shared, used and adapted to everyone and every goal.

These are the tools to steer yourself "there." Achieving high-level performance, excellence and success is certainly something great and wonderful. Of course, the next day, after the celebration wears off, you will face the mirror and ask:

Now what?

And, ideally, you will know what to do.

Chapter 1

Don't Fear the Obvious

I'VE BEEN LUCKY. I have had the opportunity to train, visit and party with excellent coaches, outstanding athletes and training partners. To find the keys to progress and success. I like to talk with people who have walked the walk before me.

Sometimes, the answer is to do the opposite of what everyone else is doing. Years ago, Bill Koch lectured at the Salt Lake City REI, where he discussed "inventing" a form of cross-country skiing that completely changed the sport. He skated past his competitors, and the sport morphed on the spot. He also trained differently from everyone else, using his focus on hard intervals versus junk long-distance training.

I call this a contrarian approach, and I love it. There's an ebook, which you can grab for free from *danjohn.net*, about discus throwing that discusses how I approach coaching the event by *not* throwing the discus. Now *that* is the definition of contrarian.

And, I love it. I love it.

But, being contrarian is nearly worthless in most areas of life. Generally, the answer to most of our questions will be fairly straightforward. The answer is boring. The answer is obvious.

Steven D. Levitt and Stephen J. Dubner have a series of books they call *Freakonomics*. These are fascinating books, and some readers find things that make them want to say and do horrible things to the authors. But, like my professor used to tell us in my college econ class, there is not a lot of "nice" in economics.

Three points leaped off the pages as I read *Freakonomics*. It was at that moment that I realized that economics, in addition to geometry, might be the two best fields of study for a coach.

The three points:

+ *Knowing what to measure simplifies life.*
+ *Conventional wisdom is usually wrong.*
+ *Fear of the obvious—Don't be afraid to do the obvious!*

I would like to apologize to the authors for taking such an excellent book and summing it up so pithily.

Knowing what to measure simplifies life

One of the reasons I enjoy coaching track and field is that there is almost no judging. No one votes on a winner. There is neither a swimsuit contest nor a Q&A after the event to help the judges decide.

It's distance and it's time. The victor jumps or throws the farthest. In the races, the winner is the first across the finish line. It's pretty simple stuff.

When judges are involved, universally we all boo the decision.

Track and field coaches know what to measure. I was at an event and a woman told me she high jumped in high school. I asked about her best. The number was impressive and we talked about how she went to a major regional championship and even considered competing past college.

The husband asked, "How did you know she was good?"

She jumped "this high."

It's pretty simple: Knowing what to measure lets you know what is working or not working—good or bad, excellent or poor. I knew she was very good because her mark was very good.

Strength coaches should stick to load. Certainly, mastery of movements and solid techniques are important, but load is how we measure things.

With the human body being such an amazing, adaptable thing, measuring weight on the scale is rarely a good idea. You learn nothing about lean body mass from stepping on the scale.

The waistline measurement is a key for the fitness trainer. Almost always, when the waistline measurement goes down, good things are happening with fat loss. Yes, you can buy and use very expensive machines to determine bodyfat percentages, but the waistline measurement usually does the same job far cheaper.

So:

> *Track coaches measure time and distance.*
>
> *Strength coaches measure load.*
>
> *Personal trainers measure waistlines.*

You might be reading this and wondering: What should I measure?

This is where the rest of the discussion will lead us. Sometimes in team sports, what to measure demands some thought. But for longevity, you could simply measure quality years of life.

Find something to measure. Measure it. Apply practice and programming. Measure again.

Then, assess to determine whether or not it's a good measurement!

Conventional wisdom is usually wrong

One of the more annoying habits of modern parents is to come to practice and ask if the kids are doing cardio. Technically, if hearts are beating, the kids are doing cardio.

I have a new answer: "Well, today we are focusing on the lymphatic system."

That shuts everyone up, as most people only have a vague notion of this important system, as opposed to the "unimportant systems" that keep us alive, and we can continue running 400-meter repeats.

Conventional wisdom in strength and conditioning seems to be this:

- There is a need for an arm day, but few understand the need for a leg day or back day.
- Mindless aerobic work leads to mastery in sports through sweating.
- Core work, or lots of ab crunches, improves athletic ability.
- Warming up and cooling down are crucial to performance.
- It is an absolute must for the athlete to look the part, both physically and materially, with proper expensive gear.

None of these are true. In fact, none of these are even that important in the big picture, but I sure like how well outfitted the athletes of the current generation are when they show up to practice. They might not be able to run a lap or do a pullup, but, wow, do they look good in their matching apparel.

Fads tend to dominate the fitness world. Jogging, yoga, aerobics, step aerobics, Jazzercize, Nautilus and all the rest of the workouts that shall not be named dominate training, fitness and fat loss until we all come to realize these options simply don't work.

That's a problem: We start doing something that is really hard, makes us sweaty and maybe makes us puke but rarely delivers the benefits promised.

But, these methods *have* to work! The people on the commercial got great results!

And…that is the issue with conventional wisdom: It's based on commercials, popular magazines and hearsay. Conventional wisdom tends to be so right sometimes and so wrong at other times.

The problem with conventional wisdom is that there is no measurement. Next week in the hair salon, there will be a new magazine; the TV doctor will find a new herb, and someone with shinier pants will be selling a new program.

Fear of the obvious

I have based my life on trusting the obvious answers first. My overview of being a track and field coach is:

Throwers throw.

Jumpers jump.

Hurdlers hurdle.

Sprinters sprint.

If you can prove to me that anything works beyond this, I am all ears. But, until that day, you can coach a teen to the finals of the state meet using these simple truths.

I know. These are obvious.

Lift weights to get stronger. Fast to lose bodyfat. Stretch to get flexible. Read a lot to be well read.

Obvious. I wish I could sell it to you.

Most of us have an odd fear of the obvious. Somehow it isn't sexy enough. It's not flashy enough.

But, it works. The answers to most of life's questions are obvious. And we all seem to hate this. We all seem to fear this. Most of what works in life is so obvious, we refuse to put our arms around it and apply it.

Percy Cerutty

Percy Cerutty is one of my coaching heroes. I was struggling as a throws coach when I went "all in" and signed up, as a camper, to the John Powell Discus Camp at Dennison University in Granville, Ohio. During one of our rare hours off, I walked into the library and went to the sports section, where I found one of Cerutty's books…a rare find in 1993.

His insights changed my career. From his work, I developed *Easy Strength,* while adding more medicine-ball games, more gymnastics and an understanding that the athlete needs to use imagination to become elite.

He emphasized "thinking" before training. Famously, he said:

> *"While work does do things, it's intelligent*
> *work that does superior things."*

Intelligent work.

Growing up, there was a phrase used for everything in life: *Look before you leap.* A few minutes of planning trumps years of rehab from lack of planning.

Intelligent work means using your brain before you rely on pain. As I often tell people: You might have one more injury, but do you have one more recovery?

You can run with this as far as you want:

- You might have one more offseason, but do you have one more season?
- You might have one more hard workout, but do you have one more recovery?
- You might have one more "hold my beer and watch this," but do you have one more chance of escaping the alligator's jaws?

Hard work does amazing things. Intelligent work does even better things.

Intelligent work...intelligent coaching

Once we embrace the idea that intelligent work trumps...well, whatever is the opposite of intelligent work—we soon understand that intelligent coaching is the best thing coaches can do.

The value of using the brain first means several things:

- More efficient technique
- Injury avoidance
- Faster recovery (injury avoidance...*is this redundant?*)
- Faster...longer...stronger...better...any other word with "er" at the end
- Longer "youth"
- Better performance

I can always tell when people have been well coached. Their technique seems to save energy. Their approach is simple. The execution seems flawless. There isn't a lot of wasted energy. As we say in sports: Nothing "bleeds out."

Including the athlete!

Learning from the one-percenters

Years ago, I sat in an audience and listened as two rabid speakers assailed each other's positions, character, moral code and parentage. Finally, a third speaker was allowed a moment. He paused and said:

> *"I represent the radical middle. I reflect what 98% of the population believes about (this topic). We can learn from the one percent on both sides, but the rest of us need to have our voices heard."*

Radical middle. The one-percenters.

The concepts changed my political thinking, but more important to this discussion, the concepts changed my coaching.

I tell my young interns—and all my audiences—this simple wish: I wish all of the fitness trainers and coaches would help an underserved community. There are plenty of people who need help. Help them.

A coach I spend time with, Taylor Lewis, works with the two most famous professional baseball players in the sport. If I said their names, you would know them, but I won't. Taylor then hops in his car and heads off to help people with cystic fibrosis. When Taylor talks, you should listen.

Why?

When Taylor says something works, it's because it works with the elite of the elite of sport and also with people struggling every day to do the basics of life…like breathing. Trust me, if something Taylor does works to improve the best MLB players in history *and* helps people struggling with CF, it's going to work for the rest of us, too.

In addition to elite athletes, I also work with people who have multiple sclerosis. Thomas DeLorme worked with injured WWII vets…and polio victims. Most of the great insights in training come when we test both ends of the spectrum: the underserved and struggling, and the top of the performance pile.

Taylor always calls his clients with CF athletes because they strive, as the original definition of "athlete" reminds us, for the prize. For people with any physical (or mental or…) issues, the prize is quality of life.

My book *Can You Go?* attempted to find a simple way to assess the general population—these are the people I call "everybody else." These are the 98 percent who need to address one or more of these three issues:

- Body composition
- Strength
- Mobility

The 1-2-3-4 Assessment in *Can You Go?* gives a general idea of where the typical client needs to focus for a few weeks. The client's actual goal is secondary, as the focus is not on what the client *wants,* but on what the client *needs.*

It always sounds harsh, but more often than not, most clients truly don't know the answer to the question, "What's your goal?" Most people spout off vague concepts like "lose weight" that don't even make sense in the big picture of health, fitness and longevity.

Oh, you want to lose weight? Cut off a leg.

Now, if you want to change lean body mass in a positive direction, we have a different discussion.

Can You Go? was based on a three-word assessment I use for active athletes: *Can You Go?* If not, let's go home…the day, season or career is over. The assessment for performance sports is simple: Here you are! Life as an athlete is a study in the *pure present.*

Like actors and most entertainers, athletes live in the pure present. The active athlete is only as good as the last performance, the last competition or the last mark. The assessment is simple: *The last time under the spotlights is who you are right now.*

Your goal is still your goal. The journey from "here we are right now" to the goal has usually been walked before…perhaps even by you.

Generally, for active athletes I recommend 20% of their training time be spent in the weightroom getting stronger with something simple like *Easy Strength*—see Appendix Eight, page 293. The other 80% of the time should be spent practicing the sport.

But, mindlessly doing the sport will have little impact on performance. Performers need to rehearse *the problems* associated with performance. This could be rain, cold and snow, but it can also be endlessly waiting around, silly last-minute officiating gaffes, or attempts by others to unnerve you.

We can all learn from the performance athlete and the performer on stage or screen. We need to prep for this with checklists, planning and sharing experiences.

But, we also need to practice the appropriate physical tension, mental arousal and proper heart rate.

The tools of arousal control made my parenting skills better, as I learned not to shoot up to the fifth floor when my daughters "push my buttons." There are moments in life, like walking those daughters down the aisle in their weddings, where being able to control the heart rate, physical tension and mental arousal are all very good things.

I want to introduce you to how I look at this. I can support anyone's goals through four basic mental sets:

+ Shark habits
+ Pirate maps
+ Peaking, planning and programming
+ Principles

These four points will weave together and interact, depending on the specific issues of the day, week, month or year.

In addition, there are four interacting terms that deserve clarity in the field of fitness and health:

+ Health
+ Longevity
+ Fitness
+ Performance

Health, according to Phil Maffetone, is "the optimal interplay of the human organs." We determine health with blood tests, annual screenings and medical checkups.

That's it. There are far too many stories of athletes in the prime of their careers dropping dead due to some unseen health issue. We need to measure health.

Longevity is an issue of both quality and quantity. Robb Wolf once summed it up very well: Live long, drop dead. Certainly, we are living longer lives, but are we living better lives? This quickly becomes an ethical question; still, we need to ensure the quality of life, too.

Fitness is simply the ability to do a task. That's it. You don't need six-pack abs to toss a caber; in fact, being too lean might make it more difficult. If the task is a marathon and you complete it, you are simply fit for the task of running more than 26 miles. That might, by the way, impact your health and longevity to do a fitness task!

Performance comes the instant your name is called—the spotlight shines on your face and you must perform.

Performance is the key to sports, acting, dancing, music and musical theater. It probably helps politicians, teachers and anyone else who needs to persuade an audience.

To perform is the master quality for success in sports and the arts. Much can be learned from performance, even for those who never want to be on the stage.

There is one other thing to consider: Some of the best things you can do for health, longevity, fitness or performance might have to be done only once…or, at most, a few times. There are other concepts that might be ongoing.

The *Now What?* quadrants

Following those insights, I came up with the *Now What?* Grid.

Now What? Grid	Health/Longevity	Fitness/Performance
Ongoing/Permanent	Pirate Maps	Principles!
Once or a Few Times (Start/Increase/Decrease/Stop)	Shark Habits	Peaking, Planning and Programming

Health and longevity issues take up one column, and fitness and performance the other. There are some areas that overlap and you should welcome that into your thinking.

An important thing to consider

I'm convinced that human brains are hardwired to deal with famine and hard times. We seem to always fear going without—going without food, water, or gifts on Christmas morning. (That's why I am always on the "nice list.")

When attempting to change behaviors, I see a bit of a continuum from the easiest to the hardest:

> *Start*
>
> *Increase*
>
> *Decrease*
>
> *Stop*

Most of us are experts on starting things. In fact, I'm going to start fasting right now.

There! I did it!

Continuing to fast will be an issue, but, for right now, I am fasting.

Many people start a diet and exercise regimen during the first week of January. Most quit. Many people start the school year with perfect notebooks and great plans for nightly homework and early test preparation. It doesn't always happen.

Starting seems to be pretty easy for us to do. Increasing things is a bit harder. Good nutritionists, like those I first encountered in the early 1980s, had us focus on:

> *More protein*
>
> *More vegetables*
>
> *More water*

Asking people to eat more seems like a fairly simple task. Throughout my career, I have mentioned this three-part formula to dozens, if not hundreds, of athletes. One would think the responses would be universally "Yes, of course!"

Sorry, no.

If you wish to use this list, prepare for the following:

"Where do you find protein?"

"What exactly are vegetables?"

"Like, water?"

I have a policy *not* to write letters of recommendation for athletes who ask questions like these. I'm not sure you want your surgeon or dentist being this clueless about the basics.

Decreasing is where things get difficult. Most of us know the value of cutting back on carbohydrates, desserts, sweets, cheat meals, booze and a long list of other things. Okay, then: Decrease those things!

I must say, that was easy to type.

Easy to type and hard to do. Most of the issues we have with things to decrease are that they're mindless habits. I have a few ideas about dealing with those. So as to not keep you in suspense: Empty your cupboards and home of all the junk and never buy any again.

You're welcome.

Stopping. Stopping is tough.

I used to occasionally visit AA meetings with a guy called Crazy Jerry. I always left smelling of cigarettes and bad coffee, so I once said, nicely:

"It might be an idea to stop smoking, too."

CJ lit into me like a flamethrower. He questioned my parentage and stated some things about me that were anatomically impossible. The gist of his point was this:

> It took him every ounce of energy and free will to stop drinking. There was no room in the tank for anything else.

Stopping is *hard*. Not starting is certainly easier.

If we take these simple points and apply them to someone who weighs more than 300 pounds or just needs to shrink the waistline some, we can approach it like this:

From easiest to hardest

Show up! *(Start)*

More veggies, protein, water. Walk more. *(Increase)*

Fewer cheat meals and less TV *(Decrease)*

Stop…smoking, snacking. These are really tough!

A note on television watching: If I told you there was something in your house that was giving you diabetes, cardiovascular disease and a premature death, would you avoid it?

There is something like that. It's called the television. Avoid it.

> *"The results showed that more than two hours of TV viewing per day increased the risk of Type 2 diabetes and cardiovascular disease, and more than three hours of daily viewing increased risk of premature death. For each additional two hours of TV viewing per day, the risk of Type 2 diabetes, cardiovascular disease, and premature mortality increased by 20, 15, and 13 percent, respectively."*

~ Television Viewing and Risk of Type 2 Diabetes, Cardiovascular Disease, and All-Cause Mortality: A Meta-Analysis, Anders Grøntved, Frank B. Hu, *Journal of the American Medical Association*, June 15, 2011

Now What? Grid	Health/Longevity	Fitness/Performance
Ongoing/Permanent	Pirate Maps	Principles!
Once or a Few Times (Start/Increase/Decrease/Stop)	Shark Habits	Peaking, Planning and Programming

As you begin any march toward a goal, take a moment to discern how much starting, increasing, decreasing and stopping you will be asking yourself to do. It's easy to start walking around the world, but circling the globe will be an effort. A lot of this world is ocean, so think that through before you try to walk on water.

Generally, for health and longevity I ask you to focus on shark habits and pirate maps. Shark habits are simply those areas of life that you can take care of with one bite and they're gone. Fill out the form, gas the car, and sign the form—and you're done with it. Just do it.

One bite.

Pirate maps, Pat Flynn's excellent concept for ongoing adherence, tells us the precise steps from here to there. The buried treasure is six feet down from six paces east of the coconut tree in the cove on Blackbeard's Island.

For fitness and performance, most people fall in love with peaking, planning and programming. We all love the idea that in 12 short weeks we'll have a bikini body, be in the best condition of our lives and produce the ultimate performance.

I have discovered, as many have, that the best laid plans of mice and men…well, you know, life gets in the way of plans.

Principles literally mean "to capture first" or "to take first." *Primus* means "first" and we see it in words ranging from "prince" to "primary school." *Capere* is "to take," and most would recognize the root of "capture."

Simply, if you want to win—to take first—*focus on principles.*

I like to win.

Chapter **2**

Shark Habits

IN 1977, AT OUR FIRST TEAM meeting with the Utah State University track and field team, Coach Ralph Maughan outlined a few things that continue to shape my life. He was addressing a group of state and national champions and one Olympian.

Three statements stood out:

> *"Make yourself a slave to good habits."*

> *"Little and often over the long haul."*

> *"Lift weights three days a week, throw (or hurdle or jump or...) four days a week, for eight years."*

Each of these is true. They are right.

For now, let's look at the first one: *Make yourself a slave to good habits.*

Most people are blind to their habits. I was talking with my friend Cameron, and she noted that after a recent international trip, she was surprised at how often she had music playing during her normal life. She woke up to music, dressed to music, drove to music and worked to music.

On this trip, she had no music. In the hotel, she couldn't just flip the switch or tune to her favorite stations. The lack of noise caught her attention. She was so ingrained to having the background noise, she never noticed until there was quiet!

Most people have habits—lots of them. The television is on during meals; the radio is playing in the car, and the route to most places is so embedded that we don't even notice these as habits. Add a construction reroute one morning, and the whole day might take on a new meaning.

Reaching for a snack: *habit.*

Mindlessly staying up for another lousy "must-see" comedy: *habit.*

Endlessly surfing the web: *habit.*

Checking social media while at a restaurant: *habit.*

The bulk of your life is built around habits.

If you have been driving for years, you might not even remember the checklist of starting a car and maneuvering out of the garage to drive down the street. If you actually *think* about driving, you might be stunned at how many steps there are in the process. It will grind your gears, if you are using a manual transmission, when you actually stop to think about the left foot, right foot, hand shift and one-hand driving, all required to accelerate.

Note: Coach Maughan said "good habits."

I don't wish to correct him. Coach Maughan played professional football for the Detroit Lions, made the Olympic team as a hammer thrower, won the Nationals as a javelin thrower and won two Purple Hearts and the Bronze Star at the Battle of the Bulge. Again, I'm not correcting Coach, just adding to his legacy.

When I look at the vast expanse of time-wasting stuff in life, I think this: *Get rid of it.*

The concept is "shark habits."

One bite...and it's gone.

Fill out the form. Check the box. Don't leave the bride wondering about whether or not you're going to the wedding—RSVP!

Low on gas? Fill it up!

Better yet: When your gas tank shows half full, fill it up. I can't prove it, but there seem to be more gas stations around at half full than there are at empty.

I first heard the concept of shark habits—*one bite!*—from Robb Wolf. He was speaking to a military group and told them to take a roll of duct tape into their bedrooms to cover up all the little dots of light that infiltrate the rooms. These little warning lights for fire alarms, CO_2 alarms, alarm clocks, and all varieties of power outlets are causing sleep distress.

The upside is this: You only have to do it once. Once. One bite. That is a shark habit.

Once—one bite

Years ago, I learned the value of flossing twice a day. Here is how you make that a shark habit. For every car you own, buy a bag of floss sticks. Put them in the driver-side cubby that's usually filed with garbage, old wrappers and that thing you promised not to forget.

From now on, when you drive...floss. The sticks are right there and you can drive and floss quite safely; I have been doing this for years. Flossing is not only excellent for dental health; it's also crucial to heart health. Look it up!

I use shark habits in much of my professional and personal life. When I open an email, I answer it. Always. If I don't have time to deal with email, I don't open the account. I believe in touching postal mail only once. I go through the mail and discard the junk (sadly, most of my mail is junk these days). If it requires attention, I immediately deal with it.

If the bride wants to know if we're coming to the reception, I let her know…now. If it's a bill, I pay it. If a telephone call needs to be made, I make the call. That's all. Done.

I fail on this sometimes. Oddly, when I do forget to do something, like redo my annual business application, I somehow lose the form and it costs me hours of backtracking, waiting on hold, and dealing with unhelpful people at the state office.

During my hour on hold, I recommit to those shark habits.

I'm convinced that many of our festive traditions are rooted in shark habits. For example, years ago, my family found ourselves with nothing to do on Thanksgiving Friday. It's a four-day weekend for school children, and Thursday is the big day. The following day, we had two bored girls in the house, so we decided to set up for Christmas.

Since then, Thanksgiving Friday has been the sacred day when all of the holiday cheer is layered into our home. The whole house is transformed into the Spirit of Christmas.

More recently, we added a new tradition when we finish the decorating: Wine and Prime.

We crack open a bottle (or two) of wine and go online to shop for Christmas. We use free shipping that day and take care of everyone on our shopping lists. In full candor and apology, if you were down the list a bit, I might not be sure why we bought you that for Christmas last year.

Shark habits are the ultimate in "do this." Basically, for anything that can be done swiftly, *do it now!*

One bite.

For health, I believe every gym and every family should have a list of phone numbers taped to the wall:

Medical doctor (general practitioner)

Dentist

Eye doctor

Veterinarian

Trust me about the vet: You might never get a client to go to the dentist twice a year, but, if Fluffy gets sick, that person wants a good vet on speed dial.

If you are a gym owner or a personal trainer, you need to cultivate relationships with doctors, dentists, eye doctors and various therapists. If you have a client who needs a doctor, pick up the phone, call and stand there while the client makes the appointment.

There is a shark habit that works for me with my medical team: When leaving the office after an appointment, as the nurse asks, "Do you want to set up the next appointment?" I always say, "Yes."

No, I don't have my calendar with me.

No, I don't know what I'm doing six months from now on a Tuesday at 1:30.

But, yes, I make that appointment! My doctors now text, email and call to remind me about the appointment, so I let them use their time and energy to get me where I need to be.

Other shark habits for general health include signing up for a basic first-aid class, CPR, the Heimlich Maneuver and how to use a defibrillator. Actually, it's probably wiser to get everyone you know to take these courses, as you want *them* prepared when *you* need one of these emergency interventions.

Often, you need only one class to catch up on the basics of all of these skills.

If you are an athlete, shark habits are pretty simple and obvious to the experienced participant:

* Buy the shoes.
* Buy the equipment.
* Renew the membership.
* Send the check for the event.
* Set up the flight, the rental car and the hotel.
* Show up!

For people new to a sport, this list can be a bit of a burden as they try to sort through all the options, especially equipment. If you don't believe me, talk to a cycling enthusiast if you doubt how many options there are in the sport.

As the years go on, the membership renewal automatically shows up and you simply have to click "Renew."

As the years go on, you will have friends to share rides and meals.

As the years go on, it gets easier and easier to show up as the shark habits begin to take over so much of the early efforts to get things done.

Shark habits eliminate clutter

I read an article a long time ago that claimed something that shocked me: The average person eats only 14 foods a week. Think about that—only 14 foods.

At a workshop, we were given a key to better nutrition—to list the foods we ate each week—not the portions—nor were we to seek the carbohydrate load, the micronutrients or the quality of the food—simply, we were asked to list the foods.

If this is your list, you should be doing fine:

Eggs

Salmon

Tuna

Oatmeal

Blueberries

Almonds

Chicken

Apples

Grapefruit

Cottage cheese

Vegetables

Armed with this information, I decided to make two things to make my family's health better: a shopping list and a weekly menu.

I still use the shopping list on the fridge. Here you go:

Meat

Poultry

Sausage

Bacon

Fish

Shellfish (if you can eat it)

Canned tuna

Salmon

Eggs (buy them in the five-dozen cartons)

Heavy cream (for coffee)

Real butter

Cheese

Salad greens (and everything you can eat raw)

Lemons and limes (to sweeten drinks and squeeze on fish and salads)

Herbs and spices

Olive oil

The best in-season fruit

There is a little box for basic toiletries and household supplies.

When I shop, I load up on what we need for the menu for the week. Here:

Monday:
Steak and salad

Tuesday:
Viking enchiladas

Wednesday:
Irish jambalaya (Champagne Wednesday!)

Thursday:
Breakfast for dinner

Friday:
Hang and graze

Saturday:
Special rotating meal

Sunday:
Whatever looked good when shopping

There is never a question like "What should I eat?" The answer is already in the pot!

I do this with weekly chores, monthly chores and yearly chores, too.

I take this seriously. I recently found a black polo shirt that travels well, doesn't wrinkle and looks good.

I bought 16 of those shirts.

Why 16? It's all the site had in my size. They are all the same look and design. I own two pairs of expensive jeans from a brand that guarantees I can squat in them. I own four pairs of shoes with the word "Free" in the name, and I can honestly tell you the price was far from free.

Why? Why wear the same thing on every road trip, talk and gathering? Among the reasons, I find "No one really cares what I wear" to "It takes me about a minute to pack for a 10-day trip."

It comes down to this: I pull them out of my closet, pop them in my lightweight, compact carryon and I am ready to go. I don't think a lot when I pack.

I learned this shark habit from my experiences in the Middle East. Back then, when I packed for the trip, I had lots of luggage. In the luggage was clothing. And clothing has great value, except I brought very few things that would make me travel better. Even a lifter gets tired of carrying luggage.

One night I wrote the following list (in very small print, I notice, 30-plus years later):

Nail clippers *(This is still true. Nails grow!)*

Hand laundry detergent *(I didn't understand laundry rooms then.)*

Towel *(This is still true. I have an expensive micro towel.)*

Swiss army knife *(The list pre-dates 9/11.)*

1 Dress pants *(Maybe…it depends.)*

1 Hiking shorts *(I use black workout shorts now, but it's still basically true.)*

1 Swimsuit *(This is still true—two matching trunks that I rotate.)*

2 Mesh underwear *(The kind I use now weren't invented yet!)*

2 Tank tops *(I understand the point, but I don't bring them now.)*

3 T-shirts from home *(Not anymore. Maybe for after hours at the hotel.)*

1 Dress shirt *(Not anymore…for me, anyway.)*

1 Tie *(I stopped wearing ties when I made a certain goal.)*

1 Walking shoes *(I just use my "free" shoes now.)*

1 Flip flops *(This is still true. I often use light water shoes.)*

Shave kit and medicines *(This is the most elaborate part of my packing. Think ahead.)*

Hat *(I haven't thought of that in a while.)*

Sunglasses *(These really can be important, so yes.)*

Backpack *(I get the kind that rolls into the size of a softball.)*

1 Bota bag *(For water. Now we have lots of options. So, yes.)*

1 Excellent guide book *(Book! I still agree with that. Devices might fail me.)*

1 Camera with film *(Some of you will have to look up "film.")*

Lip balm *(It is such an issue in the desert. Yes. And small.)*

Flashlight *(Always. The traveler's best friend.)*

Socks *(I'm still searching for the perfect travel socks.)*

Today, I pack every possible connector for my computer, an international power hook-up and packets of coffees and teas for morning and evening. Each is in its own little sack provided by first-class service when I fly international. Don't throw those sacks away.

Shirts, socks, sacks…and I'm packed.

Shark habits save…

Shark habits save time. Shark habits save mental overload.

An important point: Shark habits don't judge whether or not something is important, unimportant, trivial or the key to life, living and the universe.

I think weddings are very important, for example. As the father of the bride, I once had to make a phone call to a family member a few weeks ahead of my daughter's wedding.

"Are you coming to Kelly and Andrew's wedding?"

"Well, yes, you must know we will be coming."

"Why didn't you RSVP?"

"Well, you know we will be coming."

"Okay…how many?"

"Oh, I don't know who will show up…maybe the kids, maybe their kids, sometimes they bring friends…"

The reception was a sit-down meal, and every guest cost enough money to feed a family of four at a chain restaurant. The difference between two guests and 20 from one family was information we could have used.

Letting the bride know whether or not you are coming is important. Lots of things we do each and every day are important. Many of them you probably never even think about. We need to grasp what's important.

In order to have a good day, you probably need a fair share of "tions" in your day:

> *Emotions*
>
> *Digestions*
>
> *Eliminations*
>
> *Progressions*
>
> *Inspirations…and we can go on and on.*

Some things we think about, and some things are automatic. Certain factors determine what is truly important *now* versus what we might call "a nice thing to do."

Tim Carr, one of the smartest men in education, teaches Maslow's *Hierarchy of Needs* with a fun story:

> *Imagine you are going scuba diving. You go because it allows you to be one with nature, enjoy the beauty and frolic on a beach holiday after months of hard work saving money to fly to this paradise. During the dive, a very hungry shark or sea monster shows up and you*

hide behind a rock, keeping the rock between you and this denizen of the deep. You suddenly notice you are running out of air and need to get back to the surface. The pang of lack of air trumps the danger, the danger trumps the beauty and...

You just learned the basics of Maslow's *Hierarchy of Needs.* Everything was important:

Hard work

Vacation

Beauty and bliss

The reminder that nature likes to eat

Protection

Air

The shark in this story teaches us about shark habits and importance: Most of the things we do are "important." Perhaps filling out a form is not important to you, but it's important to the poor person who has to figure out how much food to buy or how many chairs to set up.

Fill out the form. Be part of the solution, not the problem.

Chapter 3

Shark Habits and Pirate Maps

I HAVE TALKED IN DEPTH about how shark habits can make a huge difference in physical health. See the doctor, go to the dentist, floss your teeth and you know the rest—shark habits will do wonders for health, longevity, fitness and performance.

More important, though, shark habits will do wonders for mental health.

Shark habits and longevity

One day at the Pacifica Barbell Club gym, Dick Notmeyer asked me a question. Now, to understand Dick, a man who changed my life by teaching me the Olympic lifts and the lessons of hard work and perseverance, you first have to realize that often, when he asked a question, he wasn't really expecting an answer.

He already had the answer.

"Danny, by percentage, what do you think are the keys to a long life?"

He went on to explain that probably 50 percent of survival into the triple digits, or close to that, is genetics. Everybody seems to know a guy who lived to 105 while smoking cigarettes and drinking moonshine. There are families who just live a long time.

Forty percent seems to be lifestyle, and that is something we can improve upon…or ruin.

And, sadly, 10 percent is pure luck.

If you left a minute later, you might have been in that accident or might have been the one-millionth customer and won the prize. It happens. There is no training for improving luck, outside of *Felix Felicis*, the liquid luck from the *Harry Potter* books.

The secret to living a long life might simply be "Don't die." Good advice, but hard to quantify.

There seem to be three things—and maybe a fourth, and you already know them all—that contribute to longevity:

- Don't smoke.
- Wear your seatbelt and helmet, if appropriate.
- Learn to fall and recover from a fall.
- Never say, "Hold my beer and watch this."

I often tell people that since I don't commute, the most dangerous part of my day, statistically, is showering. After 55, nutritional decisions don't matter nearly as much as safety precautions against falling or collisions.

Certainly, your teenage child's eating and drinking habits and decisions in the early 20s concerning beer and pizza will have an impact on that 50-something body, but after 55, not getting broken trumps any magic food or supplement. Safety in the shower, walking on ice and double-checking for traffic is far more important than getting the right vitamins.

Bill Gifford's book *Spring Chicken* and companion website, *springchickenbook.com*, offers some simple advice to increase longevity:

> *Caloric restriction leads to a longer life. Intermittent fasting does the same thing...easier.*

> *Exercising 100 minutes a week adds seven years to life.*

So...

Start fasting.

Start walking.

He also notes that coffee and red wine are helpful in longevity, as well as a few supplements and one or two medicines.

Yes: Don't die. To improve our time here on this marvelous planet, there are some simple steps of both prevention and promotion that can keep us living longer.

The corollary to Coach Maughan's famous insight would be this:

> *Make yourself a slave to shark habits.*

Practice taking things off the table, clearing the clutter and checking the box. Become more proactive.

Use imperative sentences when it comes to much of life:

> *Go!*

> *Call!*

> *Do!*

Some of the best lines in Hollywood history are imperative sentences:

> "Leave the gun. Take the cannoli." (*The Godfather*)
>
> "Go ahead, make my day." (*Sudden Impact*)
>
> Westley: "Give us the gate key."
>
> Yellin: "I have no gate key."
>
> Inigo Montoya: "Fezzik, tear his arms off."
>
> Yellin: "Oh, you mean this gate key?" (*The Princess Bride*)

For clients who need to bring their waistline down, here are some imperatives—some shark habits—to get things going:

- Call the eye doctor, dentist, MD
- Print a shopping list and menu
- Clean out the cupboards (dump the junk!)
- Buy appropriate food
- Prep meals
- Get a dog that loves exercise

To summarize shark habits, learn to take things off the table and put them away.

Pirate maps for ongoing change

If you floss your teeth, eat well, sleep well and avoid being devoured or blown up, you are pushing yourself in the right direction for longevity. If you use shark habits for all of life's little "check the box" moments, you are going to find yourself on the path to living long and living well.

Don't forget: You want both quantity and quality on the path to a long life.

To keep on the path, I argue for what Pat Flynn calls "pirate maps." Pat is famous for his bullet-point lists of things to do to accomplish a goal. Yes, these are like checklists. Yes, these are like "to-do" lists. Yes, these are like "Do this!" lists.

But, they are a little different.

Pat teaches us:

> *"I give the analogy of how a fitness program should be like a treasure map. A treasure map is valuable not because it's 100 pages long. It's valuable because it marks a clear path from A to B.*
>
> *"It is a short, written plan, hardly amounting to more than a page, with clear instructions on how to achieve the goal."*

It can be a plan for practically any long-term goal. Here would be one for lifelong financial planning:

- Remain debt-free.
- Maintain an emergency fund with enough to cover minor problems (and make it easily accessible).
- Save some money every month for some distant "fortune fund."
- Buy quality goods and services.
- Maintain your health with proper care and medical and dental check-ups.
- Choose wisely when it comes to matters of the heart.
- Invest deeply in your and your spouse's (!) education and career advancement.

I'm not sure there is a surprise on this list or anything that would make your great-grandma wonder about or disagree with in principle.

In the June/July 2016 edition of *AARP*, financial wizard Warren Buffet said the same things:

- ✦ Hold plenty of cash for emergencies…and opportunities.
- ✦ Buy and hold.
- ✦ Embrace the boring (this is a basic truth of coaching, too).
- ✦ Stick with what you know (another basic truth of coaching).

There were other points, but you get the idea: The truths of one field usually carry over into every other endeavor.

Tiffini, my wife, has this great insight from her career with the Department of Treasury: *Don't over-paper things.*

It's a simple concept: The more you write, the more notes and handouts and copies you produce, the less your audience, clients and people can hear.

How to *not* over-paper weight lifting

We tend to overcomplicate everything in life. Tell people to "eat clean," and they ask for a 500-page manual to explain it. To "get in shape" might take several thick volumes of work to detail everything.

But, to get strong is one of the easiest things I know.

If you want to get stronger, lift weights.

The best method I know is simply "One-Two-Three." It's an old method that has again seen the light of day.

Pick a big movement.

- Push: bench or military press
- Pull: pullup
- Squat: front squat or back squat
- Hinge: deadlift

Find a load you can do for five reps. It's going to vary for most of us, but a normal trainee will find that 80% of max is about right. Now, follow this rep scheme:

1-2-3

Do a single, rest a bit, do a double, rest a bit, then do a triple. That's six total reps—the rep quality should all be excellent. For a quick workout, run through this three times: *1-2-3-1-2-3-1-2-3.* For a tough day, go through this five times for a total of 30 reps.

Never miss and never chase fatigue. Try to dominate each and every set. You want the weight to feel light and easy. Inch that load up over a few workouts. As we discover in throwing the shot or discus, inching your effortless efforts up a bit seems to increase our best.

This is an old method of strength training that has been ignored for a while. You can train as you usually do and just sprinkle these throughout the workout. Many have found this does wonders for the pullup, but experiment using it with the squat or deadlift, too.

Getting stronger in these key lifts is the "secret" to power, mass and leanness. Speed up your progress by backing off a bit, but strive to increase load.

The moment you begin churning out encyclopedia-sized tracts on a topic, you lose people's attention. If you've ever worked in an office, as I did in the 1990s, you know that this was never covered better than the 1999 film *Office Space:*

> Dom Portwood: *Hi, Peter. What's happening? We need to talk about your* TPS *reports.*
>
> Peter Gibbons: *Yeah. The coversheet. I know, I know. Uh, Bill talked to me about it.*
>
> Dom Portwood: *Yeah. Did you get that memo?*
>
> Peter Gibbons: *Yeah. I got the memo. And I understand the policy. And the problem is just that I forgot the one time. And I've already taken care of it, so it's not even really a problem anymore.*
>
> Dom Portwood: *Ah! Yeah. It's just that we're putting new coversheets on all the* TPS *reports before they go out. So if you could go ahead and try to remember to do that from now on, that'd be great. All right!*

Many fitness books have this same issue: There are massive tracts on anatomy, physiology and endocrinology that don't get read by the typical reader and add nothing to the question of how to build lean body mass and lose bodyfat.

Let me share my favorite of Pat Flynn's pirate maps. This one is basically how to live a solid, healthy and fit life:

- Start your day by thanking someone or something.
- Have 20–30 grams of protein within 30 minutes of waking up.
- Occasionally don't have any breakfast. Fast.
- Follow the 100/100/10 rule: Have 100 grams of protein a day, 100 grams of carbs (or less) and 10 (or so) glasses of water.
- Strength train three to five days a week. Get sweaty two or three days a week.
- Walk more than you ride. Take the stairs. Park farther away.

+ Don't be afraid to stretch whatever's tight.
+ Have a sleep ritual.
+ Train consistently for progress. Add variety for plateaus and randomness for fun.

This list is as clear and simple as "Walk north five paces from the palm tree next to the red rock on Victory Island, dig down six feet and find the buried treasure!"

Some of my cookbooks work like pirate maps. I have several that focus on five ingredients or a single-pot or slow-cooker meal. Anything that needs to be done daily, or at least weekly, lends itself to this kind of approach.

Pirate maps are a fun practice for people in any business or field. To make one, you would make a short list of things that will bring about the most joy/profit/gains/delight.

Although pertaining to a sport—something that would fit better on the performance side—Vincent Tanner came up with this pirate map for powerlifting, the sport comprised of three lifts: the squat, the bench press and the deadlift.

+ Focus on the squat, bench press and deadlift.
+ Use the "same but different" exercises.
+ For barbell lifts, use low reps—everything else, use bodybuilder reps. (The 20/80 rule!)
+ Have a heavy day (slow) and a light day (fast).
+ Triceps, hamstrings, lats and abs can't be too strong.
+ You might never have to deadlift heavy outside of a meet.
+ Back off when you need to.

That's brilliant. He summed practically every school of thought in the sport in seven points.

And, we all know this: For many people, this is far too simple... let's complicate it!

Checklists and to-do lists

Recently, I was asked for my pirate map for a "lost coach." I thought that was funny, as a lost coach certainly can use a map.

My pirate map:

- Stretch what is tightening.
- Strengthen what is weakening.
- Have beautiful technique.
- Eat more protein and veggies.
- Drink more water and take fish oil.
- Compete with your strengths, but work on your weaknesses.
- Make a difference.

Pirate maps *do* tend to be like checklists and to-do lists. But, the difference is that pirate maps live a long life. Each statement must reflect a daily to-do list that will be true today, tomorrow and two decades from now.

There is nothing wrong with to-do lists, but compare this to-do list to an ongoing pirate map:

1. Mow the lawn.
2. Pick up the prescription.
3. Drop Harry off at the cat groomers.
4. Wish Nellie a happy birthday.

These tend to be one-off activities and, generally, Nellie is going to celebrate only one birthday a year. The exception is my daughter, Kelly, who reminds us to send gifts on her half-birthday.

In addition, a pirate map is *not* is a Christmas list. Now, there is a need for those in both giving and receiving gifts for Christmas, but pirate maps are different. I swear, when I work with some clients and athletes, I get Christmas lists—

I want to be a:

> *Ballerina*
>
> *Pro beach volleyball player*
>
> *Lawyer*
>
> *Doctor*
>
> *Fighter pilot*
>
> *NFL player…*
>
> *I want a pony*

Oddly, I can get you a pony. That one…I can do that one!

This is a common thing with high school athletes. I have this joke about high school kids and their answers when asked, "Where are you considering going to college?"

> *As a freshman: Harvard or Yale*
>
> *As a sophomore: Michigan or USC*
>
> *As a junior: the local state school*
>
> *As a senior: the local junior college…or Bob's Burger Joint*

I can buy you a pony, but all those other dreams and goals are going to take a lot of focus, energy and even some luck. And, to be honest, many goals take some excellent genetic potential.

The other great thing about pirate maps is ongoing assessment. Pirate maps are like that '70s song "Enough is enough is enough is enough—I can't go on."

Assessing shark habits

For clarity, shark habits are assessed as "Did you do it or not?" If the answer is "No," go do it!

Assessing pirate maps

Years ago, Tiffini came home from work with a book, Charles Coonradt's *The Game of Work*. At the time, I was working as a high school teacher, where our school had recently run through several principals who lasted only a year or so. Then, as now, my mantra for leadership is "Lead me, follow me, or get out of my way."

Coonradt perfectly explained my problem with these short-term principals:

> *"Another common field of play in business is shaped like an amoeba—a random, globular shape. It describes the employee's understanding of what he or she thinks is expected, and the only problem is that it wiggles and jiggles and changes shape. When something goes wrong that the employee didn't think was his or her responsibility, sure enough, someone points it out as his or her responsibility on the amoeba."*

I had been working for principals who saw jobs in this amoeba paradigm, especially when things went wrong. And things always seem to go wrong in a building filled with 1,000 teenagers.

This reflects what I see in the area of nutrition. Recently, I saw a famous name in the fitness field link to a site that was "anti-Paleo diet." Paleo dieting is the notion that one should eat like a hunter-gatherer from 10,000 years ago: meat, fish, veggies, in-season fruits, water and then do lots of walking around in nature.

The article claimed that what I just wrote was wrong. This is the amoeba in the fitness industry; just when you thought you found the right thing to eat for breakfast, you were told breakfast is bad for you!

How do we keep things straight?

Coonradt recommends, from the sporting world, to imagine work like a field of play. There are "out of bounds" that could range from stealing from the cash register to inappropriate sexual behaviors. We then march upward from what he calls the "Safety Zone" to "Get Off My Back" to, finally, "Paydirt," the achievement of the goal.

The safety zone as a strength coach is key: What is a reasonable but safe and sound approach to fitness that can last a lifetime? What is the least one can do to get the most benefit?

GOMB, Get Off My Back, is something akin to what I learned from Coach Ralph Maughan at Utah State University.

If Coach had an athlete who would lift weights three days a week and show up to practice five days a week through the fall and winter, he didn't push, pull or beat this athlete into doing more. The mantra was "little and often over the long haul."

Training intelligently for four years beats those occasional bouts of lunatic high-intensity training that can lead to injuries, illness and stagnation.

In Coonradt's world, one needs to find measurements to help employees know when they are on track and doing a good job. If they are meeting those standards, well, GOMB!

Get off my back!

That is enough. GOMB.

Coonradt's final idea of "Paydirt" is where a person goes over and above the call of duty. In performance, this is great. Here is where we want you to push the limits of your genetic potential.

49

With pirate maps, we might find that doing too much too often might hurt long-term. As we often say in fitness, we might be writing checks we can't cash a few years from now.

When assessing pirate maps, consider the points of GOMB.

If the client is eight for eight or nine for nine on the list, that's great, GOMB! Now, if certain elements are being skipped, ignored or encouraging revolt, go back to the item, and ask this question:

> *Is this crucial to ongoing health or longevity or fitness and performance?*

If not, why is it there?

If it's crucial, intervene. For most things, using a timer to alert the person to meditate, for example, seems to work. I use an app that pings me a daily reminder to take a minute of quiet. For fat-loss clients, I ask them to stop twice a day and be mindful. A friendly ping works wonders here.

If it's something like a morning protein shake, either make the drink the night before you go to bed or buy small protein drinks that can be popped open and consumed while still yawning.

In other words, if something on a pirate map is being skipped and it's important enough to keep, set up bells, whistles and pings to ensure compliance. Don't think about it; do it.

Compliance

The compliance chart for pirate maps:

1. **If the client or athlete is doing everything on the pirate map—**

    GOMB

2. **If something is not being addressed—**

    Address it.

3. **If we are going above and beyond—**
    Celebrate it!

For someone who is striving to get a waist measurement to half of height or less or is striving to get under 300 pounds, here's the pirate map for that (thanks to fat-loss coach Josh Hillis for this one):

+ Keep a food journal.
+ Count your cheat meals.
+ Eat protein and vegetables, and drink water at every meal.
+ Walk every day.
+ Lift weights.
+ Surround yourself with people who support you.
+ Hang around with people who are on the same journey.

For a time-management shark habit and pirate-map plan, see Appendix One on page 225.

To summarize the pirate-map concept:

Do THIS!...from now on.

Chapter 4

Plans, Programs and Peaking

FITNESS, AS I HAVE PREACHED since the 1980s, is the ability to do a task. That's it. If you can't walk up a flight of stairs but can throw the shot farther than everyone else, you win the shot put.

Fitness gets sold as six-pack abs and the ability to do a bunch of burpees. Burpees, by the way, were invented by a man named Royal Burpee, who wouldn't understand the fascination of doing this nice little assessment for more than a few repetitions.

Until there's an Olympic burpee champion, it's just an exercise. Doing 10,000 burpees or anything similar doesn't measure fitness, but it might be a measurement of your need to get a life.

The fitness field sells better when people sweat, puke and flail. Flailing has great value for flailing, but it pales when compared to the march toward mastery.

Mastery, the effortless effort of true excellence, doesn't look like what we see in commercials or advertisements for exercise. No, it looks beautiful.

It looks…right.

Instead, most people ask for the three Ps:

> *Plans*
>
> *Programs*
>
> *Peaks*

And, this is the one time where most people get it exactly right: Once or twice in your life, you can achieve astounding fitness goals by following a program precisely and enjoying the benefits six to twelve weeks or months down the road.

Like a fat-blitz diet, which all of us have started and few of us have finished, it's wonderful to dial in everything for a short time and reap the benefits.

I can understand the reason to buy into this stuff. Universally, there is a time limit to getting the best results of your life:

> *Two Weeks to Six-Pack Abs*
>
> *90DayXcellence*
>
> *Six-Week Bikini Bootcamp*

I was kicked out of the Bikini Bootcamp twice: I assumed we would be training in bikinis and, boy, did I get that wrong.

Any time you see "overnight" or "instantly" in fitness, you know you are dealing with this issue. I don't mind annual "focused" training, like some extra focus on diet after the holidays or before a vacation or a wedding, but it's impossible to always live in famine mode.

Yet this is what people ask for from fitness professionals.

The problem with peaking and planning and programming is as old as the Yiddish proverb, *Mann traoch, Gott Lauch.*

Man plans, God laughs!

Most people I know have entered into marvelous training or diet plans, only to discover that life gets in the way. It's fun to caution an enthusiastic newbie who is convinced that the *Six-Week Soviet Squat* program is going to be challenging. What we can't always explain well enough has to do with climbing the stairs in a day or two, and the difficulty of descending onto the toilet to relieve oneself.

Life gets in the way of plans. Cars break down, weather changes, people die and phone calls happen that impact the training program of the best and brightest. Plan all you want, but life has a way of cutting us down.

People think I'm joking when I note that it's a rare week when I don't get some form of this email:

> *"If you could just send a program and eating plan to get me into the best shape of my life..."*

Without any frame of reference, background, life history or basic facts, this person wants a simple plan to get in "the best shape of my life." Don't even think "the best shape *for what?*" Just realize that this is, once again, magic-wand thinking.

Without Gandalf and Dumbledore to the rescue, I don't have the answers here.

The "twos" ladder

When it comes to planning, programs and peaking, I have "two" thoughts. You will get the joke in a moment.

55

Often, people offer me money to give them some perfect plan. It's easy money, but I always refuse. For me, writing a program for someone takes a lot of time and energy. Sure, we all know that. But, it also takes a vision. I call this vision the "Twos Ladder," as we need to agree and understand each other for a fair number of steps before I can even begin talking about five sets of five reps or three sets of three.

The foundation is two decades. Twenty years from now, what do you want to be doing? Usually, two decades is far enough away that the glitz and glamour of the professional sports or the bikini body for the all-inclusive vacation will be past. Hopefully not long past, but generally, 20 years is far enough ahead that we can look at health and longevity as more important than abs and biceps.

I don't want training injuries to ruin the quality of life in 20 years. Yes, of course, there will be hurt, pain, injury and agony, but let's look down the line to see if this is going to be worth it.

It's the foundational question: *What do you want to be like and be doing in 20 years?*

Stepping up to asking what we want in two years usually gets us to the wishing well. Two years is long enough to gain mass, lean out, improve technique and develop the system to get a set of goals.

Then there are some wonderful follow-up questions. My favorite: *Will achieving this goal make you successful?*

Success is one thing and achieving a goal is another; wise people will tell you this truth. Looking ahead two years also allows us to dream a bit about the perfect future.

There will be flying cars.

As we often say in fitness, most people tend to exaggerate what can be done in one day and under-appreciate how much can be done in one year. Miracles can be achieved in two years with a logical, reasonable approach.

From here, I take it short term: What can we do in the next two weeks? We can't fully make ourselves "slaves to good habits," as Coach Maughan preached, but we can take care of the small things. Is the bedroom dark and quiet? Do we have the right equipment, including shoes? Do we have a means to get to the training facilities? Do we have a bottle so we can drink more water every day?

These are the little questions that make or break the two-week goals. Sometimes, shopping beats training. If we need something, from equipment to supplements, the sooner we deal with it, the better. Let's circle a problem and spend two weeks addressing it.

In the next two years, you will have 52 two-week blocks to improve things. If you even improve a few things on the pirate map toward your goals, you will probably be living your dreams.

Then, I address today. What can we do today? What do you know? Can you do the Olympic lifts? Can you hinge and squat?

If not, that's what we do.

Where we begin

We begin with the fundamental human movements—for a complete overview, see Appendix Four on page 251. We begin with small movements that will lead to complex movements. We teach, we learn and we relearn.

So, today…*today,* we are going to focus on the fundamentals, the basics, and just get better. We will strive for mastery and beauty. We will be reasonable on the reps, sets, load and distance. We will practice. We will train.

We will prepare ourselves to be better in the future.

Tomorrow, in many ways, is more important than today. The most valuable thing you can do is show up. And, from there, keep showing up. Three-hundred moderate and progressive training sessions a year trumps three really hard days during the first week of January.

As fine as today's workout might be, tomorrow's is even more important.

This is a bit of advice I tell my older trainees: Tomorrow? Ah, tomorrow. Tomorrow, we will vomit, puke and sweat. We will break all of our records and end up in a sweaty spot on the floor. We will go to the edge and beyond and show no fear.

To prepare for tomorrow, today we will focus on fundamental work with appropriate and reasonable sets, reps, distance and load. We will leave feeling better than when we arrived. We will practice. We will train!

And, when you show up tomorrow, I will tell you this: Today, we will focus on fundamental work with appropriate and reasonable sets, reps, distance and load. We will leave feeling better than when we arrived. We will practice. We will train!

You see, tomorrow never comes.

Before I agree to outline a plan, a program or a peak, I will walk you through the two-ladders process. It doesn't take very long, but we'll establish what is important first and foremost.

I'm not that good at programming, but I know people who are skilled at this process. For the client who wants to get under 300 pounds or get the waistline to half of body height (at most), I don't know anyone better than Greg O'Gallagher of Kinobody.

For fat loss—his program is called *Aggressive Fat Loss*—he outlines in great detail:

1. Intermittent fasting
2. Strategic black coffee to make fasting effortless
3. Eat two meals per day (one very big meal and one smaller meal)

4. Strategic fruit snacks to make eating two meals per day effortless

5. Performing three intense workouts per week to maintain or even increase muscle

6. Performing low-intensity exercise on rest days to support fat loss without increasing appetite or cutting into recovery

This is all dialed in...do the program exactly!

Summarizing *Plans, Programs and Peaking* is simple:

Do *this,* until...

You do this program until you get your body-comp goals. You do this plan for 90 days. Doing this plan, you peak on the day of the Nationals or the Worlds.

Peaking programs

Marty Gallagher is a master of peaking programs. I was honored to work alongside him, with Pavel Tsatsouline, training a group of America's elite Special Forces.

Marty uses Civil War General Nathan Bedford Forrest's great insight about strategy to explain planning, programming and peaking:

"Git thar the furst-est with the most-est."

Marty streamlines this for the athlete:

"Get the most-est for the least-est."

Marty learned his peaking and planning system from Hugh Cassidy, the first super-heavy world powerlifting champion in 1972, and used this same program to teach two of the best powerlifters of all time, Kirk Karwoski and Ed Coan.

Although the program relates to strength training, the principles can be used for anything from walking programs to fat-loss plans. The strength program is based on these truths:

- Once a week, work up to a single top set in each of the four core exercises.
- Success is dependent upon achieving technical perfection in these lifts.
- Each week for 12 successive weeks strategically push the top-set poundage.

To sum:

Concentrate on doing fewer things better.

Periodization

With these truths in hand, Marty periodizes the training. Periodization is simply preplanning the poundage, the reps and sets for each workout for the next three or four months.

Some general insights about periodization:

- Start off far lighter than you expect—50–65% (at most!) the first weeks.
- All lifts must have perfect technique (this is the toughest of all).
- Never miss the top lift; to ensure this, never start off too heavy.
- The stronger the lifter, the lower the weekly increases.

Marty also believes in preplanning calories, calories burned, cardio work and bodyweight. As he noted, if you're doing the bodyweight periodization method, he doesn't care what you have to do the day or night before a weigh-in to make your weight.

One quickly learns it's far easier to be smart all week rather than straining to lose extra pounds in just a few hours.

Periodization is reverse engineering—working backward from the goal planned out into the future. The goal needs to be realistic and the time frame has to be specific.

If you want to lose 10 pounds in 10 weeks—a reasonable goal—grab a calendar and some paper and work backward, scheduling a one-pound loss each week. It might be better to plan a two-pound loss during a few of those weeks and one or two maintenance weeks, just to keep some variety in the program. He believes change should be drastic, not minor, so it might even be fun, in this example, to schedule a three-pound weight loss one week.

In strength programs, he might go three weeks of eight reps, drop to five, and then attack another three weeks. The weight would increase a bit each week, and the fourth week might be "easy" because, even with the increased load, the reps are fewer.

This process works very well for the elite athlete and the typical weight-loss client. The key is the reverse engineering—starting with the end in mind, as business author Stephen Covey once noted.

I wrote a whimsical (okay, sarcastic) article years ago about New Year's resolutions:

> *I have a goal for you. Oh, not for this January or even the next few months. Next January 1st, I want you to weigh one pound less than you do today. That's my goal for you.*
>
> *Now, if you have to fast from Thanksgiving until New Year's Day, I am fine with that. If you have to sit in a sauna in plastic all through New Year's Day, I am comfortable with that, too.*

Wait? What do I hear? Is it scoffing and coughing about our next New Year's Feast? Too little work for this man, this beast? (Hats off to Dr. Seuss here.)

If you do the math and can remember that one pound is 3,500 calories, you need to cut only nine calories out of your daily intake!

There is a sassy soft drink that advertises itself as "Just One Calorie!" If you are drinking 18 of them a day now, simply cut back to nine a day for the next year and, POOF, your pound will be gone!

That's all I am asking: one pound less next year.

I still stand fast that losing one pound a year is a better plan than most of the nonsense I read daily. Liver-cleansing your way to a 20-pound loss is just not in the cards for most of us.

Marty warns us to start conservatively, start light and start with a goal at first that is so reasonable and easy that we gain some emotional momentum as we work through the process.

Yes, I believe in planning, programming and peaking.

Yes, I believe that these methods work.

No, I don't think most people put the time and energy into *planning the planning.*

If you have a line in the sand, like a beach vacation, a wedding or the Nationals, plan away. Program it. Try to peak.

"Do this!"…until your vacation, wedding or the Nationals. I applaud you. But then…

Now what?

Assessing plans, programs and peaks is fairly simple. After you finish, did you get the body comp, squat or mass goals promised by the program? Did you peak at the most important competition of the year, decade or career?

If the answer is "Yes," well done! That was a good program! Share it with friends and family, perhaps buy into it with an affiliate program, or offer to buy a share in the company.

When I was doing the Soviet squat cycle, a six-week program of squatting three times a week, I turned to my training partner with a look of distress.

"What's wrong?"

"I have to do that five more times!"

The program for the day called for me to do six sets of six reps with 80% of my best front squat. I had just finished the first one, and I couldn't believe I had to do five more sets. I made a vow: If this program didn't work, I would fly to Moscow and punch every Soviet I could find.

The program worked as promised. It's very difficult, but my squats improved.

The same is true for the Velocity Diet. This diet is only six protein shakes a day, but the upside is you get to enjoy a meal once a week.

One meal. Once a week.

Almost daily, I threatened the diet's designer, Chris Shuggart, with physical harm if I didn't get a six pack. The program worked wonders, and I actually ended up with an eight pack.

There is a subtle point you may be missing: I have *finished* very difficult training and diet protocols. The programs worked because I did exactly what the system demanded.

Every so often, I get emailed questions about my *Mass Made Simple* program. The writer will ask if he can substitute leg presses for the squats. In truth, you can do anything you want any time you want, but no, that's not MMS. If you don't eat the protein,

63

shovel food down your throat, and do the difficult 14 workouts, you didn't do MMS.

This is my knock on plans, programs and peaking: Few people actually finish them. It's really difficult to assess most TV infomercial fitness programs, because rarely do people do the whole program.

Oh, people *buy* the products; they just don't finish the program. Like treadmills, those DVDs (plus those bonuses valued at $1000) end up on the top shelf behind the diet books or over by the ThighBlaster 5000.

This is why I am a fan of Marty's reverse-engineering principle. If you can't lose 10 pounds a week for 10 weeks, trying losing a pound a week for 10 weeks.

It's reasonable. It works. It just doesn't sell well.

Peaking plans, those elaborate spreadsheets detailing the road to perfection at a given time and place, must also be judged through this lens.

I'm not a fan of peaking programs, as they tend to fail with one simple insight: Everyone knows that the Nationals, Worlds or Olympics will be happening on *this* day and at *this* hour. So, why doesn't every performer hit a lifetime best at these contests…or, at least, a seasonal best?

If a sports team discusses peaking for the championship game, most of us would roll our eyes and make scoffing sounds, as there are no guarantees that our beloved team will even make it to the Super Bowl or the National Championships.

The answer is simple: Performance demands more than physical peaking.

Elite performance demands principle-based training.

One more point about programs

A while back, I was in Scotland with Mark Fisher of Mark Fisher Fitness. Now, Mark has ignited the fitness world with his gym and his methods of building community. His people are "ninjas," and the gym is their clubhouse. (Trust me, this is the tame stuff.)

His program *Snatched in Six Weeks* became an NYC phenomenon. Getting on the program roster was as hard as getting opening night seats on Broadway. "Snatched," by the way, is not the Olympic lifting or kettlebell term: Here, it's the way Broadway dancers refer to each other when they're in great shape. "Ripped," "buffed" and "snatched" are the same relative terms.

As I was addressing the audience at that Scotland event, I told them what I love best about *Snatched in Six Weeks* is that the program moved from a six-week challenge—and God knows we all love them—to a pirate map for ongoing physique goals. When he heard that, Mark had a look of both shock and amazement. This often happens: Good programs show us the path to the buried treasure.

If something, like drinking a lot of water and sleeping eight hours a night is a good idea for six weeks, it's probably a good idea "from now on!"

Good programs lead to pirate maps. And good programs and pirate maps lead to principles.

Principles

I told you how Coach Ralph Maughan, WWII vet, NFL player and Olympian, stood in front of us and told us the secrets to success:

"Make yourself a slave to good habits."

"Little and often over the long haul."

> *"Lift weights three days a week; throw (or hurdle or jump or...) four days a week, for eight years."*

Coach was giving us the secrets to success in life, as well as collegiate track and field. He was teaching us how to win, how to succeed and how to take first.

Anytime you start discussing "to take first," you are discussing principles. Now, I grade my students down when they use the dictionary, but in the case of principles, it's illuminating:

The word "principle" comes from the Latin principium, *literally "that which is first."*

It is also argued that the "ciple" part of the word is from the same root as "capture," which gives me the nod to claim: "Principle" means "to take first!"

Principles are those magic keys, golden nuggets and perfect diamonds that are the secret to success in any endeavor. To master and measure and monitor principles and success (or failure) becomes a matrix, a flow chart to improved performance. Principles are the universal standards that support excellence.

You might have had a principle wash over you and you missed it. I heard this in hurdling the first time I was taught the basics:

> *"Attack with your lead knee."*

Later, Coach Maughan applied the same phrase to our college hurdlers and then noted that it's true in the high jump, long jump, pole vault and triple jump. Principles have a funny way of working in all kinds of endeavors.

The next one, *little and often over the long haul,* is as true in finance and relationships as it is in performance. Over the years, Dick Notmeyer's advice to me about maintaining a tranquil mind would help me perform better on the lifting platform.

It was also perfect advice for handling two teenage daughters.

I own a copy of one of the original American football coaching books, *Heisman on Football.* The book is certainly dated in some aspects, as my copy is from 1935, but the principles stand the test of time. To win in football, Heisman expected three things:

- ♦ Block
- ♦ Tackle
- ♦ Fall on the ball

Blocking, tackling and keeping possession of the ball remain the three keys to the game nearly a century later, regardless of thousands of rule and equipment changes in the intervening years.

When I first met Dick Notmeyer, he explained the "secret" of great Olympic lifters:

- ♦ Strong legs
- ♦ Powerful pull
- ♦ Tranquil mind

When I am asked about the principles for a strength coach, I use these:

- ♦ Standards *(Is the person up to the necessary standards?)*
- ♦ Gaps *(Are you doing push, pull, hinge, squat, loaded carry and the sixth movement?)*
- ♦ Everything else from the actual sport

A couple of years ago, I wrote a book about my assessment process for athletes, literally just the question: *Can You Go?* If you know your game and have prepared for days, months, years or decades, all I can really ask on game day is *Can you go?*

If it's "Yes," then go! If not, well, we're done.

As much as I love principles, they don't always work perfectly. For that client who weighs more than 300 pounds and needs to lose some of the weight, principles, sadly, come up short.

Art De Vany famously answered a "How do I lose fat?" question with "Don't get fat in the first place." Although it might seem mean spirited, it's correct and could be a tool in working with college-aged or 20-something adults.

Mad TV once spoofed the "most true" principle of fat loss: Eat less, move more. A woman was angry because they had "Eat less" on one side of the card and "Move more" on the other.

She had to flip it over.

So, yes, principles are the heart and soul of performance and performance sports. But, for areas of life like health, longevity and fat loss, shark habits and pirate maps might be better. True, a pirate map for fat loss will end up with "Eat less, move more" principles, but most people will follow Pat Flynn's list on page 44 better than the underlying principle.

Principles can be summed as: "To take first...do this!"

And, have some method to measure your ability to "do this!"

Shortcuts and principles

I have nothing against shortcuts. My entire coaching career is based on finding shortcuts. The late Tommy Kono, Olympic champion in weightlifting and a bodybuilding Mr. Universe, said it best about the American system:

> *"The American system is to get to the goal as simply and quickly as one possibly can."*

Focusing on principles is actually a shortcut. Eliminating needless thought, adopting shark habits, for example, is also a shortcut. Being first often gets you the best parking space, the best seat and some time to plot, plan and prepare for the meeting or event.

Focusing on principles allows a different measure of victory. We often get caught up in the idea that only the Super Bowl or World Cup or Olympic Champ was successful. Measuring principles allows not only a vision of more success—we achieved 98% of our goal—but it also ensures the realities of competition, both in sports and in life.

+ There are genetic gifts your opposition might have in greater supply than you...speed, height, looks.
+ There are financial boons to living in some places or being from certain areas.
+ There is luck. That's just how the ball bounces.

Some shortcuts involve illegal, unethical, unhealthy and immoral choices.

With my two-decade question, this discussion unfolds in an interesting way. One of my competitors told me about his anabolic-steroid use during his career, and told me that once he became a father and embraced religion, he found himself at an odd decision: "Do I tell my kids the truth?"

Frankly, I don't care, but this is part of principle-based training: There are also life principles.

+ Do you want a doctor whose helicopter mom did all of his high school assignments and who got into medical school because of a large donation by Grandpa?
+ Do you want your pilot to have figured out ways around the alcohol and drug tests?
+ Do you want to win something and then later have it taken away by a positive drug test?

I believe in strategic shortcuts: The sooner we decide what is core, what is key, what is crucial, what are the principles…the sooner we can find success.

Some of my best successes as a coach were in the 1990s, when I worked at a school with high academic standards and no facilities in which to train. We couldn't do things like the other teams and instead developed the model of one-hour training sessions focused on the key principles of training the discus, shot and javelin.

You can see the full details in the free book, *A Contrarian Approach to the Discus,* which you can get here:

http://danjohn.net/pdfs/book.pdf

I am convinced that thinking (sadly, a lost art) is the finest shortcut in the world. Thinking about the principles, in any endeavor, is the key to true success.

To repeat:

Principles can be summed as "To take first…do this!"

And, have some method of measuring your ability to "do this!"

A simple, but important point

Shark habits—and this should come as no surprise to anyone—are *habits.* Pirate maps are an attempt to circle certain aspects of life and pave the road to habits.

In health and longevity, habits are far better than hiring a band of cheerleaders to rah-rah you to a tighter tummy. Having said this, I certainly do not discount the idea that having a permanent posse of encouraging cheerleaders would lead you to success in body composition. I was just worrying about the expenses of flying, commuting and the meal service for that support crew.

Habits are wonderful. In the areas of health and longevity, the best habit I can think of is to surround yourself with dozens, if not hundreds, of people who are striving for the same goals as you. When you live on the Island of Misfit Low-Carb People, you will probably stick to your low-carb goals better.

Community trumps individual free will each and every time.

When it comes to success with programs and principles, sadly, it's one more "P": pain.

Failure clarifies errors in principles. When we ask, "Did you throw far?" and you answer "No," there is pain. When you fail at a principle, we can probably backtrack to pain rather quickly.

Pain is a wonderful tool for a coach. I wouldn't say it's fun to use, but, wow, does pain work.

Reminding a recently divorced wife about her ex-husband's hot new girlfriend is a great way to keep the divorcee on a diet and exercise program. Pain is a wonderful lever to push the whole Earth in the direction you want it to move.

If a weakness causes a defeat, a program of six to twelve brutal weeks might be the answer. And, the pain of failure will be the engine driving the completion of that program.

Here's the thing: In an odd way, failure is the engine of success. It gives a person the will to focus on principles and stick to a program. Happy, well-adjusted people don't always do well in performance.

Tony Robbins has made a living using people's pain or pleasure to make instant change—ideally for the better. I applaud that.

But in performance, pain seems to be the key to application. Most great athletes and performers certainly like to win—but they *hate* losing.

If you get the chance in life to make yourself a slave to good habits and find a community to support those good habits, I applaud you. In a sense, as we used to say, you lucked out.

If you wish to be great in performance—and I'm not sure I completely understand this point—seek failure and pain, and use that pain to navigate you toward success.

Odd. Strange. And true.

Chapter 5

Assessing Principles by Assessing Performance

YEARS AGO, GENERAL KURT NEUBAUER, United States Air Force, retired, and I became great friends. Like most people in the military officer corps, he understands my emphasis on thinking things through before applying a hammer or chainsaw. I owe him a great debt on this project, as he is the one who took this "principles" idea to the next logical and often ignored step:

Assess them!

The general has spent a lot of time in fighter jets and then teaching and leading fighter pilots. The assessment he uses is "The Five Whys."

The "Five Whys"

Perhaps this example isn't for the faint-hearted, but in aerial combat, life and death rests on the razor's edge. After a training mission, there are two...and only two...questions:

> *Did you kill?*
>
> *Did you survive?*

In actual combat, there is no second question.

If the answer to the first question is "Yes," we move on to the second question. If the answer to that one is also "Yes," we are done assessing.

I have greatly simplified things, but this is how we assess principles. It's an easy formula:

Did you...(whatever the plan was)? Yes or no.

If "Yes," move along.

If "No," ask "Why not?"

Continue asking "Why?" four more times, as necessary, to find an issue that can be fixed, addressed or practiced.

Let's go through some real examples from my coaching experience. The principle in our throwing group is "Throw far or die!" The second part is an attempt at both humor and the seriousness of what we do.

Me: "Did you throw far?"

Athlete: "No."

Me: "Why not?"

Athlete: "I left my throwing shoes at home and I..."

Stop right there. Why did the athlete forget throwing shoes? It's an important piece of equipment for a thrower...right up there with shorts and the implement.

I had mentioned checklists to this thrower many times and... there, it's right there.

I mentioned it to the thrower, but the thrower doesn't have a checklist.

Paul Northway made a checklist, had it laminated and put it on his gym bag like a luggage tag. Before every competition, he sat down in his bedroom, pulled out every item and repacked everything, individually noting everything on the checklist.

For the record, Paul never forgot his throwing shoes.

The 10th hurdle

One of three principles of coaching the hurdles is "The race is the 10th hurdle."

Coach: "How did you do on the 10th hurdle?"

Athlete: "I crashed into it."

Coach: "Why?"

Athlete: "I was really tired and chopped my steps."

Coach: "Why?"

Athlete: "During practice, I haven't been..."

Perfect. The athlete came up with the answer.

It could be conditioning. That's one very good answer. But it could be something else, and the experienced coach needs to be prepared for it.

The hurdle races in track and field are difficult to train for. In my experience, a hurdler needs about 14 races in a season, races of various levels of pressure, to get used to the "noise" of a track meet. Rarely in training does the hurdler have the crowds, the starting gun, the crashing of other athletes and the elbows and bodies flying around after spills into the hurdles.

A hurdle coach needs to artificially produce this environment. In practice, most hurdlers go for only three hurdles and then slow up and go back to the starting line to begin again. But, the race is *ten* hurdles. If you put strips of duct tape on the ground for hurdles four through ten and have the hurdler finish the distance, you will be simulating competition.

And having sprinters run next to the hurdler in the other lanes will mimic some of the noise of competition.

Noise

"Noise" is one my favorite coaching terms. I learned it from my political-science professor, Robert Hoover. Students would ask questions about how someone should have known that this or that was going to happen.

The classic was, "Didn't anyone tell FDR the Japanese were going to attack?"

The answer?

Noise.

The president had probably been told that every single day for a few years. Couldn't "they" see the Great Depression/WWII/Vietnam/whatever coming?

Noise.

I immediately applied the noise concept to training.

"Didn't you know you needed to throw the discus farther to win the Nationals?"

"Why didn't you do your best?"

Noise.

So, now I literally train "noise."

I add noise to my athletes' practices. We find lesser competitions to discover noise issues. We strive to eliminate noise as the answer.

This will be expanded in detail later (see page 135), but the answer is to provide more noise to get the athlete used to it.

The answer to "Why?" should lead us to options that can be trained, practiced and worked out.

Team sports have an additional issue: The team!

Let's go back to John Heisman. He said that "block, tackle, and fall on the ball" were the principles to winning football.

Me: "Did we tackle?"

Coach: "We made the tackles 64 out of 67 plays and lost 21-0."

For those who don't understand American football, if you miss a tackle and the other team scores, they basically get seven points. Seven points times three missed tackles is 21 points.

We missed three tackles.

Me: "Why?"

The answer could be conditioning, technique or poor pursuit. After watching the films or just remembering those key plays, we can address these issues in practice.

The more we study the key moments in sports or any performance based on the principles we agree that are core to the pursuit, the clearer our training focus will be so we can address the actual problems.

Sometimes athletes decide to do more than the job (admirable), but they forget to do their jobs first (problematic).

Coach: "Did you make the tackle?"

Athlete: "No."

Coach: "Why?"

Athlete: "I had an bad angle and was out of position."

Coach: "Why?"

Athlete: "I let myself get caught up in traffic and couldn't get around it."

Coach: "Why?"

Athlete: "I lined up too close to the line of scrimmage."

Coach: "Why?"

Athlete: "They were killing us with that one play over and over, and I cheated up to stop it."

Coach: "Why?"

Athlete: "Billy was not plugging his gap."

Ah.

That took a while, but this is common in team sports: Someone tries to play super hero and be two humans at once. We may have to rethink Billy at his position or go back to our basic team concept.

It would also be very wise to ask Billy what was going on.

"Coach, I was exhausted, but I was told if I let you know I was tired, I would never play again."

Ah.

My fault.

What Billy was thinking was not true—he was "told wrong," and it cost us a score.

We need better clarity on our substitution policy. We need to find out how the team communicates our policies. Billy's conditioning is a factor, yes, but there are always layers to addressing problems. The upside of this process is that you now have, as a coach, a career-long addition to your checklist: Address substitution policies!

It is best to stick to the script (Why? Why? Why? Why? Why?), but dialogue becomes part of assessment, especially when a team or athlete is struggling.

Free throws when tired

For basketball, one of the principles is "Make free throws when tired."

I would ask the coach of a struggling team this question:

Me: "Did you make free throws when tired?"

Coach: "No."

Me: "Why?"

Coach: "We do free-throw competitions in practice all the time. We put pressure on the athletes, and they're great…80 percent of the attempts are good on our worst day!"

Me: "Do they shoot the free throws with the appropriately high heart rate, you know, like after sprints or during conditioning or late in the practice session?"

Coach: "No. It's so important, so we do it first thing."

Me (logical follow-up): "So, when fresh, they make them. When tired, they don't."

Please let me stop here, Coach. I'm begging you to see the point that they are not practicing free throws when tired.

We are assessing performance, and we are trying to find a solution to problems. We want to practice, from now and in the future, the issues that impact performance.

The answer "I don't know" has to be discussed.

If it's too close to the performance and the athlete is still processing emotions from a poor competition, "I don't know" might just mean "I need to stop the screaming in my head."

After an appropriate amount of time, the more important or public the failure, the more time that might be needed for an athlete to clear the mind and assess the performance.

We would begin with the Five Whys.

In a team sport, there are times that "I don't know" may lead to "You don't play."

Coach: "Why did you miss that block?"

Athlete: "I don't know."

Coach: "Was the problem that you didn't know whom to block? Was it a technical issue or something else?"

Athlete: "I don't know."

Coach: "Was it something we can train?"

Athlete: "I don't know."

Coach: "Okay, you are no longer playing…Yosehansky, you are now the starting guard."

These are *not* evaluations—these are assessments

My daughter, Kelly, started teaching before she graduated from college and quickly rose up the ladder of educational leadership. She told me an important thing about the best way to evaluate things like workshops, seminars and in-service gatherings. I am skipping several parts for clarity.

Basically, she is looking at three things:

+ Initial evaluation
+ Information that the teacher has learned and could recall later
+ The impact on the students from the teacher participating in the event

The initial evaluation is generally useless and mostly worthless. I used to run a thousand-person gathering called "The Congress," and people insisted that we have evaluations. I asked those people who demanded the evals to be on the Evaluation Committee.

Odd thing: Not one of these people ever again insisted on evaluations.

Why?

Evaluations are worthless.

"The room was too hot."

"The room was too cold."

"There weren't enough bathrooms."

"The breaks weren't long enough."

One year, we had buffet lines for lunch and we had the complaint:

"There was too much food."

In a self-serve buffet line, it's not my problem if you put too much food on your plate.

The second phase is information the teacher participant could remember and use, at some level, after the workshop. I am often amazed how much I learn at workshops. A few weeks later, someone nicely asks me what I learned.

"Ummmmm...."

It's embarrassing and true. I have gone to multi-day events and have come home more confused than when I left. Now, there are other times when the event is truly life changing. I always put the John Powell Discus Camp and the Russian Kettlebell Certification (RKC) events at the top of these lists.

Other times, I might take copious notes on all kinds of things and retain no knowledge of what the point of all that writing was in the first place.

The true evaluation of any educational moment is what the student or the participant actually learns.

When I got back from the first discus camp and also from the RKC, I transformed the training of my athletes. Others would later go to these workshops and note:

"This is just like practice."

A good workshop or learning experience should be measured by the impact upon the student.

There is a parallel here: When assessing principles, we are trying to see what the student or athlete learned and nothing else. If it's not sticking, we need to find other ways to make it stick.

The principle matrix

The "Five Whys" are the principle matrix. Basically, it's this: Did we do X?

No.

Why?

Blah

Why?

Blah Blah

Why?

Blah Blah Blah!

From this discussion:

1. *Blah Blah Blah* leads us to the important issue.

2. The important issue is the thing we can practice.

3. From here, we address how we can practice this thing.

The coach and the athlete must have a tool for measurement. Track and field and swimming are easy: Did you go higher, faster or farther? The strength sports of power and Olympic lifting are also easy: Did you total more in this competition?

In American football, the principles of tackle, block and fall on the ball need a measurement. Let's take our earlier example:

Measuring tackles

How many total plays…and how many total tackles?

How many missed tackles? (Technical issues?)

How about those times we weren't even close to tackling? (Pursuit? Conditioning? Alignment?)

Now ask the "Five Whys."

And this should lead to:

What can we practice?

If you apply these *whys,* you might discover that much of what you practice doesn't support the performance. Sure, maybe whatever you're doing makes people tired, but you might not see more wins or better measurements.

One of the best coaches in history did things very different.

> *"He does not allow tackling in practice, has no play-book and does not require his players to participate in strength and conditioning workouts. There is no yelling, no tackling dummies and no whistles. His quarterbacks call most of the plays."*
>
> *"We don't have no mission statements, no big philosophy,"* John Gagliardi said.
>
> *"We just do it."*
>
> http://www.nytimes.com/2009/09/19/sports/ncaafootball/19coach.html

This is contrarian coaching, and it works well because absolute, relentless focus on principles and assessing performance through the lens of these principles de-clutters the bulk of the coaching process.

The Contrarian Approach to the Discus Throw, mentioned earlier, is based on a simple concept: "Throw far!"

The principle is "Throw far or die!"

The assessment of performance

Did you throw far? (We're assuming survival.)

> *Yes! Good.*
>
> *No? Why?*
>
> *Because…this!*

Can we train *this* with checklists, arousal training or meet preparation?

This assessment process is deeply influenced by the military academies. There are only three correct answers to a question at the academies:

> *"Yes."*
>
> *"No."*
>
> *"No excuses."*

Although I love—absolutely love…truly love—"No excuses," it doesn't work well for the assessment of principles. We must find a training or practice solution for the "No" answer.

Finally, don't beat up or analyze "yes" answers too deeply. If the athlete or performer gets the job done or the mission accomplished in a different way than usual, it might be a better idea. Sports are filled with people literally going the wrong way—Dick Fosbury in the high jump comes to mind—who have revolutionized their sports.

Chapter 6

Standards and Gaps

THE LONGER I COACH, the more I realize that performance is the easiest of the four basic things we work with in fitness: health, longevity, fitness and performance.

Performance comes down to assessing adherence to principles, trying one's best to shark-habit the bulk of life and flitting through some programs now and again to address specific issues.

Sure, there's a lot there. There is a need for mastery of a lot of areas, but overall, it comes down to:

Did you do the job?

If "No," why?

If you got cluttered with crap that could have been shark-habited out, shame on you. If we didn't practice the right things (more on this in a minute), shame on me.

Standards and gaps

People can learn a lot from strength coaches. If you don't get caught up in the countless exercises and equipment choices, it's pretty straightforward:

> *The job of the strength coach is to help people get stronger.*

As we were taught in *Think Like a Freak,* "Don't ignore the obvious."

Schools would improve overnight if we evaluated English teachers by their ability to teach English, math teachers on their competence in delivering mathematics, and postal workers on delivering the mail.

Lifting weights is the solution to getting stronger. Danny Kavadlo reminds us in *Strength Rules* that we need only three tools:

1. Something to step on

2. Something to hang from

3. Something heavy!

And, true, this is as old as Milo of Croton, who achieved superhuman strength by picking up a young bull each and every day and carrying it. He is the historical grandfather of all things lifting; he figured out progressive resistance exercise without having to run his tests with a bunch of college freshmen.

I can never just mention Milo without discussing his father-in-law, Pythagoras. Pythagoras may be best known as a geometrician and by his theory:

> *"In a right-angled triangle, the area of the square on the hypotenuse is equal to the sum of the areas of the squares of the other two sides, or... $a^2 + b^2 = c^2$."*

My life was influenced by something else Pythagoras is attributed with saying. To earn immortality:

+ Have a child
+ Plant a tree
+ Build a house
+ Write a book

As I review the list, I am reminded that there are all kinds of strength, and each of the items on this list requires many gifts.

Getting back to the strength coach, we need to adhere to two principles: standards and gaps. Both are easy to assess:

Are you up to the standard?

Do you have any gaps?

I love standards, and I collect them from all areas of fitness and performance. Some are simple, like Josh Hillis's discovery that women who can do three pullups, three dips and either squat or deadlift 135 for five tend to have made their body-comp goals.

Finnish jumpers (pole vault, high jump, long jump and triple jump) have standards that carry over into practically every sport.

Sixteen-year-old men

> *Back squat: 200 pounds*
> *Clean: 180 pounds*
> *Snatch: 115–135 pounds*

Elite open performer

> *Back squat: 350 pounds*
> *Clean: 300 pounds*
> *Snatch: 200 pounds*

Remember, these are jumpers, not American football players, rugby players or throwers. Generally this group rarely breaks more than 200 pounds in bodyweight.

Now, if you *are* a male jumper at these strength standards, you are strong enough in the weightroom. Any and all issues with your performance are on the field, both in practice and performance.

Glasgow Rugby uses a delightful matrix that should be copied and imitated by all.

Are you technically proficient?

No? Master this first.

Are you strong enough?

No? Get stronger.

Yes? Then, are you fast enough and powerful enough?

No? Get faster and more powerful.

Yes? Then, are you big enough?

No? Get bigger!

Yes? Then, do you have repeatable speed and explosion?

No? Get in shape!

Yes? Let's get out and play.

Generally, we can probably say that an elite male athlete needs:

> *Snatch: 200 pounds*
>
> *Clean: 300 pounds*

And, maybe...

> *Squat: 400 pounds*

Arthur Jones, who brought Nautilus machines to the lifting world, argued that 400 pounds would be all most of us would need to squat.

For American football, most coaches seem to argue for numbers around:

Clean: 300 pounds

Bench press: 400 pounds

Back squat: 500 pounds

If you field 90 athletes at this level of strength, the weightroom is not your problem.

For high school athletes, I use these:

Big Blue Club (boys)

One-arm bench: 32-kg kettlebell (5 right/5 left)

Standing press: 115 pounds

Power clean: 205 pounds

Deadlift: 315 pounds

Back squat: 255 pounds

Front squat: 205 pounds

Power clean and jerk: 165 pounds

Sadly, as I constantly note, there are few solid standards at my disposal for female athletes. When I first coached high school girls, I used standards from East German track and field resources.

Yes, I was probably too dumb to have the job. Those numbers for teen female athletes were solid for high school boys' football… probably good enough for junior college play.

Here are my high school female standards:

Big Silver Club (girls)

One-arm bench: 12-kg kettlebell (10 right/10 left)

Standing press: 70 pounds

Power clean: 95 pounds

Deadlift: 205 pounds

Back Squat: 135 pounds

Front squat: 95 pounds

Power clean and jerk: 75 pounds

Strength standards, and all standards actually, produce this kind of clarity. If you are strong enough, big enough, fast enough and still can't perform well enough, we need to focus somewhere beyond the realm of strength and conditioning.

Gaps walk with standards

Gaps can be explained simply:

Whatever you are not doing, DO!

When it comes to the fundamental human movements, skipping one can impede progress. When I added loaded carries to my training, my career turned around and I had the best seasons of my life...in my late 40s.

Generally, in training, people have two gaps: authentic deep squats and loaded carries. Simply adding goblet squats and basic carries can put many people right on track again. Truly, gaps walk with standards.

Long-term success in life is often held back by gaps. If you need a degree for your profession, you might not advance if you didn't take that geology class when you had the chance. Planning for retirement is best done at 20 years of age, not 70. In life, what you do not know or do not have often complicates a problem.

Does anyone remember where I put that spare tire?

Wishing for a filled spare tire while on the side of a road in the desert is probably not a good plan.

Good coaching includes constant vigilance concerning the gaps in the system. Oddly, gaps are usually easy to address:

Add them!

Assessing training gaps

Part of my career involves assessing other programs at schools and gyms. I use a simple system when looking at weekly and monthly training. First, I circle and note the number of times each of the fundamental human movements appears in the training.

The fundamental human movements (yes, I know you've seen this before):

> *Push*
>
> *Pull*
>
> *Hinge*
>
> *Squat*
>
> *Loaded carry*
>
> *Everything else!*

Usually, I am looking for groundwork in the "everything else" slot, including getups, tumbling, rolling and anything that gets people on the ground and back up.

My first review is simply to highlight the gaps in the training program. Generally, the answer inverts the above list. Missing from the programs is usually any kind of work on the floor; there are no loaded carries, and there's a lack of authentic deep squatting. I have yet to find a program lacking in bench press and curls.

Then, I tally up the variations of each movement.

Often, I find perhaps five or six push exercises per week but rarely more than a single type of squat. That's understandable, as there are few squat variations that most people can do. That's an issue for further discussion, but getting coaches to teach front, back, Zercher and overhead squats takes a level of commitment.

Groundwork is important, literally, for survival. Learning to deal with slips and falls might save your life better than peaked biceps. The hinge work, from the deadlift to the kettlebell swing, is the foundation of explosiveness and athletic movement. Loaded carries supply work capacity better than anything I have discovered in training.

Groundwork, hinges and loaded carries make good football players great. They are hard work and demand a lot of time and energy.

But for many of us, we need the hormonal changes that come with strength training. We need the increases in strength, hypertrophy and mobility that come with *proper* strength training. Luckily, the amount needed to do this is far less than most people think.

The research has been clear for 60 years: About 15–25 quality reps are all you need for strength, hypertrophy and power. In fact, this number might be too high for experienced strength athletes.

To really get a handle on ensuring that we train appropriately across the movements, apply this rule:

> *The total number of pushes (and pulls) has to equal the total number of squats. If the program calls for 15 variations of presses a week at 25 reps each, this means 375 squat movements.*

Good luck with that.

Most training programs do more than enough upper-body work. It's stunning when I add up the variations of the movements and total repetitions of pushes and pulls in most people's programs.

As I have noted before, hinges and loaded carries play by a different set of rules. Six heavy deadlifts and a 1000-swing workout are miles apart on reps and sets, but, depending on load, each can fry you for weeks.

With loaded carries, "Do them" has been my standard advice for 20 years.

Gaps and lack of foundation

Gaps also address the need for foundations and show the lack thereof.

As a strength coach, I need to focus the young athlete on loaded carries, goblet squats, pushups, ab work, flexibility and mobility methods, basic recovery tools and the importance of sleep.

Without this foundation, we will be holding back the athlete as we advance. Teaching a truly deep, authentic squat to an aging athlete is a lot of work. Teaching it to a 12-year-old is pretty simple.

Once the foundation is set, adding groundwork like tumbling and crawling can help the athlete in sports over the short term—and long term in assuring some level of safety from falls and tumbles over the rest of the life.

From here, I suggest adding the barbell world of the Olympic and powerlifts. I still include teaching the military press, abandoned by the O lifters in 1972. The snatch and the clean and jerk—the quick lifts—still do more for athlete building than anything else I know. Also, the back squat, bench press and deadlift measure absolute strength better than a million tests. These are fundamental movements for any athlete.

Although I could be talked into switching the order of barbells before kettlebells, the relative popularity of barbells makes me think, overall, that this is a better order.

With kettlebells, teach the basics: goblet squat (yes, again), swing and Turkish getup.

Feel free to add what you can teach well.

As we move to the next level, begin combining movements, mixing and matching things and striving to increase conditioning levels by increasing the amount of work done in less time. Be warned: Mastery of the movements comes before combining the movements.

This is important: As we increase the pace of work, errors multiply. Poor technique done rushed is the definition of disaster in the weightroom.

Don't be a disaster.

Advanced recovery tools such as cold, altitude chambers, massage and all the rest should be used when the athlete is dancing on the razor's edge of overtraining. Charlie Francis blocked recovery bouts into his training programs the same way most coaches plan squat training and sprint work.

Recovery efforts should be appropriate to the level of training. We tend to go overboard on recovery discussions every few years and then toss it all out. Strive to be balanced in your approach to recovery. This is the area where cost-to-benefit ratios take over the discussion.

A pedicure is relatively inexpensive where I live. Beyond the toenails, the pedicure includes a lot of skin work, plus a 15-minute foot, ankle and calf massage. Frankly, for most athletes and really, all people, this might be the best investment we can do for recovery. Building an altitude chamber in the basement for tens of thousands of dollars might not be better than a bimonthly commitment to sitting in a chair getting your feet scraped, oiled and massaged.

Finally, supplements. The nutrition stores have a great new trick: They lock up the really powerful stuff. It must be good—it's under lock and key!

Beyond coffee, most energy supplements are excuses for bad recovery, where usually the answer is "just sleep." Sure, fish oil, Vitamin D and a few others will assist in health and longevity, but most supplements are overkill and only serve to mask errors in building the foundation.

The movie *Idiocracy* gives us a great insight into the issues with supplements, especially the way most sports parents understand them:

Pvt. Joe Bowers: "What are these electrolytes? Do you even know?"

Secretary of State: "They're...what they use to make Brawndo!"

Pvt. Joe Bowers: "But why do they use them to make Brawndo?"

Secretary of Defense (raises hand after a pause): "Because Brawndo's got electrolytes."

Why do you need SuperpoweredNitro 5000? Because it's SuperpoweredNitro 5000!

I'm absolutely not against supplements, but remember: Supplements supplement.

Quality coaching an elite athlete depends on having no gaps in training. If a proper foundation has been laid, we can certainly spend more time and effort focusing on advanced nutrition, recovery and supplement tweaks.

I said "if."

If not, our task is to fill in the gaps.

My book *Intervention* was dedicated to getting the athlete to realize that gaps are stalling improvement. It's best to start early with a proper foundation and build the athlete, brick by brick, toward the highest heights of performance.

Everything else

All other qualities an athlete needs come from practicing and performing the sport. In the discus, we don't need the kind of endurance gained from running around the track; we need the endurance to throw over and over and over again.

When I was in high school, our coaches used the mile run as the standard for conditioning. Backs had to finish under seven minutes, and linemen had an additional 30 seconds. I ran a 5:51 in football cleats and probably could have done a little better.

It was hard. We had to train for the mile run, plus bench press for five reps, had a pullup test and several other things. These tests proved to the coaches that we were in shape.

Months later, after a long football season, I couldn't run the mile as fast or do the strength tests as well. But, I could play the game! I was in football shape. I could take a pounding and not bruise, hit the ground and roll back up into the play, and I could do all the extra special team sprinting without impacting my defensive skills. I was in shape for football.

Being in shape for a sport is not the same as being in shape for a test.

Don't confuse the two. Use the practice field and performance to improve conditioning.

For strength, power, flexibility and mobility, come see the strength coach.

Now What? Grid	Health/Longevity	Fitness/Performance
Ongoing/Permanent	Pirate Maps Do THIS...from now on.	Principles! To Take First... Do THIS!
Once or a Few Times	Shark Habits Take things "off the table"	Peaking, Planning and Programming Do THIS...until...

Principles help the strength coach with the sport coach

The "Do this!" principles of the strength coach are:

Standards *(Are we up to them?)*

Gaps *(Do we have any?)*

As I discussed in *Intervention,* there are times for Olympic lifts in an athlete's career and times for planks. None of the exercises are good or bad, but we need to use the right tools at the right time.

By building the foundation—the base—we can support a long career for our athletes. I see the relationship of the strength coach and the sports coach as the symbol of yin and yang. The strength coach is the black side and the sports coach is the white side.

Our joint task is to grow the athlete *out.* In a typical decade of training, we should strive to build both sides of the athlete at the same time.

Imagine a young athlete coming to a throwing ring for the first time. So much needs to be learned in the sport: the rules, the techniques, the training and the discipline of training.

Let's look at the training of this youngster:

Twelve-year-old thrower

> *Stretch 1-2-3*
>
> *Learn the lifts*

On the technical side, we break down the movement into a simple pattern and repeat it with drills. For discus throwers, we use tires, handled balls, sticks and a variety of common objects to teach the basics.

And that's about it!

Repetition is the mother of implementation. The young athlete needs to get in those learning reps.

In the weightroom, we keep things as simple as possible, too. We work the foundations: goblet squats, farmer walks and pushups. I might expand to the barbell with the power clean, the front squat and the military press (see my free ebook *From the Ground Up* via *danjohn.net* for details).

In a decade, things will look more like this:

Twenty-two-year-old thrower

> *Arousal-level training*
>
> *High-load O Lifts*
>
> *Advanced recovery*
>
> *Nutritional tweaks*

We'll discuss arousal-level training in a moment, but, basically, we try to put the athlete in as many situations as we can in training that will mimic the pressures seen during competition. We want the athlete to practice raising and lowering the arousal level as needed. We might practice sitting for long periods and then leap up and compete.

This might be the most underappreciated tool in coaching.

High-load Olympic lifts would be a key to the off-season. In fact, I have many of my throwers compete in local and regional

O lifting meets. The need for appropriate tensions and arousal in O lifting mirrors that of track and field.

At this age, advanced recovery techniques come into play. While often it's just hot tubs and cold showers, it can also be specific therapies from massage to Rolfing. These choices sometimes depend on budget as much as actual training.

I like my throwers to follow Chris Shugart's *Eat Like a Man* program. It consists of five days of nearly no carbohydrates, followed by a two-day carb fest. Competing on the fifth day of no-carbing, plus some coffee, seems to set the throwers on edge.

Be careful around them!

After the comp, pizza and beer will practically "stone" the athletes. Their smiles and happy demeanor return, and they love everything and everyone. This is great for a party but lousy for competition.

The 12-year-old needs none of this, but if the foundation has been set, the 22-year-old will thrive on these ideas.

Growing the athlete *out*...appropriately

It is relatively simple to expand a young athlete's strength side. There are dynamic exercises, ballistic exercises, plyometrics, isometrics and a world of machines and devices designed to build an athlete's engine.

It is a mistake to build up the strength, hypertrophy and power side of the yin and yang too quickly. You will end up with what Bill Witt calls "a flat tire." We need to ensure that the sports side—the techniques and skills—grow at the same rate as the strength side.

Sometimes, we can do work in the field with strength equipment. Sometimes, we can do technical work in the weightroom.

Overweight shots will help shotputters. The East Germans had a lot of research on this back in the 1970s, and they found that three things help throwers:

1. *Throw appropriately with overweight implements.*

2. *Throw a lot.*

3. *Eliminate weak links.*

These are principles supported by research. They also reflect the experience of most throws coaches.

However, studies have found that throwing things like overweight baseballs or shooting baskets with overweight basketballs *hurt* the skills. Doing overweight strength work can help performance *and* it can hurt performance. As the knight says in *Indiana Jones and the Last Crusade:*

Choose wisely.

We can often do technical work in the weightroom. Tumbling and double-kettlebell cleans feel like the game of American football with all the explosions and pounding. But, even though they look similar, having a discus thrower do dumbbell flies is *nothing* like the actual throw, which is all stretch reflex. You can mimic some things, but they might not carry over to performance.

Usually, growing the athlete out is going to be two-sided:

The strength coach will focus on standards and gaps.

The technical coach addresses everything else.

Occasionally, we will experiment with technique in the weightroom and overload in the sporting arena.

We need to dedicate the whole training team to long-term preparation and planning.

And just to ruin everything

Sport is like life. Sometimes unexpected things happen. We get hurt, we get bad breaks, and we stumble and fall. Even if you have mastery of technique, no gaps and are up to the standards, you can still lose.

In addition, some people are marvelous in training and terrible on the field of play. In American football, we use the phrase "Looks like Tarzan, plays like Jane," to give you a quick visual.

In addition, we can also make gross errors in off-season training. Yes, you can be too big and too muscular to play your position.

I'm always reminded of the NFL wide receiver who went to a bodybuilding coach in the off-season and swelled up like Mr. Universe. He got his picture on the cover of a lot of physique magazines, but never played a down of quality football again.

A wide receiver's job is to sprint and cut to a different direction. Too much mass might look good, but the ankles can take only so much. The good coach knows when enough is enough is enough.

For elite-level performance in any aspect of life, it's imperative to do more than just look the part. When the spotlight shines on your face, performance demands more than just a cute face and a pretty body…

…unless the competition is *Cute Face and Pretty Body*.

I can't do much about the former, but I can help with the latter!

Elite performance…more than looks

Under the spotlight and in front of the crowd, things are different. Performance is measured even in areas of life that aren't measured. I learned this years ago as a young teacher when our students would go off to regional drama and drill-team competitions.

"Competing" at drama seemed like an odd idea. Yet, they would return either very excited or very disheartened by the realities of competition.

I focus on three basic areas in preparing the athlete or performer:

Appropriate physical tension

Appropriate mental arousal

Appropriate heart rate

Frankly, I wish I could insist on appropriate liver function and appropriate pancreas pancreating, but the above are the three where I can actually help.

Chapter 7

APE: Accept, Practice, Experience

I'M NOT SURE I CAN SIMPLIFY the "secrets" of elite performance better than APE.

Accept the truth

Practice appropriately

Experience of others!

If the athlete knows the techniques and rules, owns the genetic gifts, remains up to the standards and is gap free, the next big question is "How does the athlete perform?"

It is my belief that performance and appropriate practice dance together. But there is a truth we need to look at.

Accept this: Performance should be BETTER than practice!

Practice is practice. This famous rant highlights the issue:

> *"It's easy to sum it up if you're just talking about practice. We're sitting here, and I'm supposed to be the franchise player, and we're talking about practice. I mean listen, we're sitting here talking about practice, not a game, not a game, not a game, but we're talking about practice. Not the game that I go out there and die for and play every game like it's my last, but we're talking about practice. How silly is that? ... Now I know that I'm supposed to lead by example and all that, but I'm not shoving that aside like it don't mean anything. I know it's important, I honestly do, but we're talking about practice.*
>
> *We're talking about practice, man. We're talking about practice. We're talking about practice. We're not talking about the game. We're talking about practice. When you come to the arena, and you see me play, you've seen me play right, you've seen me give everything I've got, but we're talking about practice right now.... Hey, I hear you, it's funny to me, too; hey, it's strange to me, too, but we're talking about practice, man, we're not even talking about the game, when it actually matters, we're talking about practice... How the hell can I make my teammates better by practicing?"*
>
> ~ Allen Iverson at a press conference on May 8, 2002

It's true. If we allowed warmups and practice in the formula for competition, I'm pretty sure a lot of gold medals and championship rings would change hands.

There are many people famous for their ability to compete and perhaps as many famous for their ability to fail on the performance stage.

I think I can help.

Accept this: Performance should be better than practice!

Learn this. Memorize this. Accept this.

Performance should be better than practice.

It is so easy to say, so easy to write and so easy to shout, but the devil, as always, is in the details.

There are three basic outcomes

I like to keep things pretty simple when addressing athletes. They're not dumb…far from it…but we need to make sure we have clarity. It's one of the reasons I don't like using complicated peaking programs: I don't want the athlete to get lost in the minutiae and miss the big picture, the big point.

Performance should be better than practice!

There are three basic outcomes, generally, when looking at the relationship between practice and performance.

A. *Performance is better than practice.*

B. *Performance is the same as practice.*

C. *Performance is worse than practice.*

A or B are fine, but C is an issue.

Three Basic Outcomes

Practice......Performance

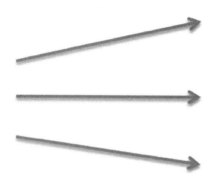

A: Performance is better than Practice

B: Performance is the same as Practice

C: Performance is less than Practice

A. Performance is better than practice

The ideal model of practice and performance is what we usually see in track and field. During the early season, the practice marks are below the prior year's performance. A lot of second-guessing happens, and some begin questioning the whole program.

Ideally, at the first meet tension and arousal will lift the athlete's marks up from practice. This begins the process of building a throw. The next week, the practice marks are better...as if hidden wires have been cut from the athletes and they can move like magic again. Performance explodes.

The next meet sees another improvement, and then the next practice marks improve, too. This continues to wave upward during the season until the athlete wonders out loud: "Why didn't I throw this far this easy early in the season?"

The Ideal Model of Performance

The Model of Practice and Performance we love to believe...and Fractals

Understanding fractals and the application to superior performance

Applying a philosophy of strength training or sports training has to be put into bite-sized pieces. There was a business cliché about 30 years ago that seems to have been lost:

How do you eat an elephant?

One bite at a time!

When I flip through a fitness magazine, I get overwhelmed. How do you do all of this as you read a typical exercise book or magazine? Yes, tumbling, foam rolling, sandbags, gymnastics work and all the Olympic sports are great and valuable.

But, how do you organize it? How do you control all of the options?

Moreover, how do we address the daily training session in light of the weekly session with an eye on the lifetime goals of the trainee?

The answer is obvious to most of us: We need to step back and look at the big picture of the life of the trainee and settle on where

109

we want to go. From there, we can drive it narrower, into perhaps a year-long approach, and from there sneak into the weekly and daily perspectives.

The word "fractals" comes to mind here. A fractal is a never-ending pattern. Fractal patterns are already familiar to everyone, since nature is full of fractals: trees, rivers, coastlines, mountains, clouds, seashells, and hurricanes. A leaf looks like a tree, a small stone looks like a mountain. If done correctly, a training day can look like a career.

Jurassic Park offers us an interesting counter point, or perhaps a warning:

> *"And that's how things are. A day is like a whole life. You start out doing one thing, but end up doing something else, plan to run an errand, but never get there. … And at the end of your life, your whole existence has the same haphazard quality, too. Your whole life has the same shape as a single day."*
>
> ~ Michael Crichton, Jurassic Park

I have two basic fractal training templates. These reflect the daily, seasonal, yearly and, perhaps, lifetime training cycle. Let's do the most basic first.

It's life. This is a training program based on our movement history.

> *We start off rolling around and crawling.*
>
> *Then, we get up on one knee.*
>
> *Then, back to the ground.*
>
> *We finally rise up and go after it for a while.*
>
> *We stumble and get back up.*

We stumble again and lie back down.

And stay there!

This is also a great template for training.

Naked Turkish getups (no weight) and bear crawls

Half-kneeling presses and half-kneeling chops

Bird dogs

Humane burpee

Mobility movements from the six-point position and half-kneeling

Naked Turkish getups

Savasana (yoga term for lying supine with calm breathing) or crocodile breathing

---

Humane Burpee

15 Swings	3 Pushups
5 Goblet squats	15 Swings
5 Pushups	2 Goblet squats
15 Swings	2 Pushups
4 Goblet squats	15 Swings
4 Pushups	1 Goblet squat
15 Swings	1 Pushup
3 Goblet squats	

Now, most athletes want to finish with something like "Last throw, best throw." We all know that saving the best for last is a key to winning championships. So, for athletes, we like to end a workout with a finisher.

This is fractal training: attempting to mimic, at some level, the big picture of the person's goals.

Coach Maughan used to preach continuous acceleration as the fundamental truth of elite performance. The key to throwing, punching and kicking is to finish fast. In throwing, the implement should come "last and fast."

Thrower's template

> *Turkish getups, bear crawls and general easy mobility work*
>
> *Slower power work: deadlifts and bench presses*
>
> *Easy dynamic stretching work*
>
> *An Olympic lift (snatches or cleans)*
>
> *Hill sprints, sled work or sprints*

There are lots of "big pictures" available, but a few minutes of looking at *your* overall goal, or that of your athletes, and stepping back to see if you can mimic it in the daily or monthly training program has great value in setting up success.

Superior athletes often seem to have a sixth sense about things. It could simply be that they recognize the pattern quicker—the fractals, the Big Picture. It's also why someone who masters one team sport, like basketball, can often carry over the patterns into another sport, like soccer. Former discus throwers pick up the Highland Games events in one day. Olympic lifters can powerlift after just hearing the rules.

Great coaching focuses on seeing the patterns and the problems early. Great coaching sees the big picture...and that is elite performance.

B. Performance is the same as practice

Things could be worse. As my old friend, Tony, used to always remind us: "Never say it could get worse, because worse always shows up at the door and gets in."

Although performance being the same as practice isn't terrible, we can do better. Certainly, in some examples, this option is fine:

We completed the mission.

For a military mission, this might be excellent, especially if we came away with no casualties and we all returned home. My statement "The goal is to keep the goal the goal" was wordplay on a military concept: "The mission is to keep the mission the mission."

"B" is difficult to coach for a simple reason: It's hard to build upon.

I need to be careful here and tread a fine line: I have had seasons where I practiced at the same level I performed...and was satisfied.

Why?

I had improved on the prior seasons or earlier performances of my career. In Highland Games competition, the higher you go in competition, the closer the competitors get to one another, both in sense of performance and friendship. With the days being so long (and hot and sunny and...), getting a solid performance might be better than having a superlative performance.

You might find that the excitement of a lifetime best may sap your energy from the next few events.

"Performance is the same as practice" might be a good template for a sport that involves multiple events: decathlon, weight pentathlon or Highland Games. Improvement comes during the focused work of the off-season.

The end of the season is not death. I like this quote for athletes:

> *"If life is nothing more than a journey to death,*
> *autumn makes sense but spring does not."*
> ~ Craig D. Lounsbrough

During the off-season, the "B" performer can improve the qualities needed to perform better the following year. This lacks the excitement of weekly or monthly improvements of "A," but these athletes know what they can do.

Athletes and performers who give you "B" performance are worthy of study. At some level, they have connected the dots between the stress of competition or performance and can deliver the goods. Their practice and performance habits might be worth emulating.

C. Performance is worse than practice

Poor Performance
tends to infect Practice

Disaster. This is what Malcolm is predicting in Jurassic Park (both books)

This is the premise of most horror and monster films. It's *not* a way to compete or perform.

"Hey, kids—look at our new home/amusement park!"

Demon/dinosaur eats someone.

"Woooo! Aren't we lucky that THAT is over?"

Demon/dinosaur eats another character.

"Well, that was bad; but NOW we're safe! Let's eat dessert."

Demon/dinosaur eats a bunch of people.

"Let's get out of here."

Scroll credits as remaining characters look back from the automobile/helicopter at the home/amusement park.

If you use this brilliant script, I demand royalties.

A training partner, Eric, went through this. He had a marvelous throw early in the season. It was effortless, and I remember how perfectly calm he was throughout the throw. It landed far beyond his best in training or in other track meets…a true lifetime best.

Our coach, not a throws coach but a very good track coach, assumed Eric would build on that throw each and every day. Eric was always put in the elite group at meets, and the pressure grew on him to improve week after week.

The more pressure he felt, the worse he threw. By the end of the season, Eric was a mess.

He quit track and field.

I have seen this happen in many areas of life: A perfect combination of events align to achieve perfection, and then we chase perfection thereafter.

Camp romance

There is a condition known as "camp romance" that's similar. A couple meets at an event where they're isolated and alone from other people in their normal lives. The new situation is intimate, exciting and perfect. They fall more deeply in love than one can imagine. Yes, yes...this is it!

Then the bus arrives to take everyone home. When camp is in the rearview mirror (the demons and the dinosaurs are running toward the fences), one of them realizes:

Oops.

Camp romance doesn't usually survive the realities of home, school, work and life. Perfect settings tend to lead to imperfect problems down the line.

To beat this point to death, I often tell people:

"If the best years of your life were in high school, you need to spend a lot more time with me."

Bruce Springsteen said it better:

> *I had a friend was a big baseball player*
>
> *back in high school*
>
> *He could throw that speedball by you*
>
> *Make you look like a fool boy*
>
> *Saw him the other night at this roadside bar*
>
> *I was walking in, he was walking out*
>
> *We went back inside sat down had a few drinks*
>
> *but all he kept talking about was*
>
> *[Chorus:]*
>
> *Glory days well they'll pass you by*

Glory days in the wink of a young girl's eye

Glory days, glory days

My book *Intervention* was partially built on this premise: Let's intervene *now* and see if we can turn this around and make the future brighter. To turn this around, of course, takes some openness and honesty.

Recently, I intervened with a top-level fighter. What caught his attention was hearing, "Performance should be better than practice."

He was candid.

He was open.

He was honest.

He was willing to change.

We talked briefly about what was going on. He had a great insight that should have been correct.

"My performance has to suffer because I always need to cut weight."

It was a wonderful assumption, but as Jim Markosian says, "Whenever you assume, you make an 'ass' of 'u' and 'me.'"

And…he says it a lot.

The real answer was just behind the green curtain from *The Wizard of Oz*. I asked the fighter to talk me through a typical fight day. He told me about a well-designed, nearly six-hour pre-fight plan that included mobility work, foam rolling, some meditation and a fair amount of exercise.

Ah. You should be able to see it now. It was follow-up question time!

"Well…what do you do on a typical non-fight training day then?"

"Oh, I just walk in and roll around a bit and get going."

Yes, it was that simple: He was leaving his performance in the warmup area. Of course, losing a fair amount of weight a few days before was impacting his abilities, but he was exacerbating the issue with this marathon warmup.

For his next fight, he was "slated to lose," when, as he told me, he decided "What the hell." He showed up a bit early for the televised event, rolled around a little, shrugged his shoulders and told someone on the side, "If I am supposed to lose, I might as well not lose the whole day."

And, of course, he won in a stunning upset, leaped up in the rankings and is now fighting for much higher purses.

Simply discussing arousal, tension and heart rate can often be illuminating.

The Successful Intervention

Just having the discussion often helps athletes as much as a full intervention. However, for most of us, we need to practice appropriately, too.

Accept this: Performance should be better than practice!

Practice appropriately...not just *more*

A strength coach can boost performance by writing a program that matches the arousal, tension and heart-rate levels that will be reflected during game time. It can be done several ways:

+ Strength and conditioning exercise choices that match the performance conditions
+ Workouts and rest periods that reflect the game pace
+ Actively practicing raising and lowering arousal, tension and heart-rate levels to give the athletes the tools to control these under the pressure of competition

Strength and conditioning exercise choices that match performance conditions

I have no issue with strength and conditioning workouts being a bit hectic for team-sport athletes. Tumbling runs mixed with Olympic lifts and some general bodyweight work reflect what goes on in most team sports. It's pandemonium, but organized pandemonium.

For an individual-sport athlete who performs in silence, the strength coach would find value in programming movements that take focus and attention. In addition, some events, like the shot put, allow a lot more rage in performance. Find lifts that allow the arousal levels to rise.

We will consider this in much more detail in a moment.

Workouts and rest periods that reflect game pace

I first learned about this from Ethan Reeve, the stellar strength coach at Wake Forest University. He came up with a brilliant idea of having his athletes do a heavy single in either an Olympic lift or a powerlift every minute on the minute for up to 45 minutes. This reflects the feeling of playing American football.

If you compete in a sport with no rest, like wrestling or Ultimate Fighting, keep moving at a high rate the whole workout. Track and field athletes might find longer rest periods appropriate to the long waits they experience between rounds in many of the events.

Actively practicing raising and lowering arousal, tension and heart-rate levels gives the athletes the tools to control these levels under the pressure of competition

This is the master tool. Teaching defenders to recover during the game and having the ability to dial up and ramp down arousal and tension depending on the job at hand is a fast track to elite performance.

It's not just *more*. *More* flexibility work. *More* conditioning. *More* strength work. *More* correctives. No.

More is easy. More is more. More doesn't always help. More can sometimes even hurt performance and ruin careers.

It is appropriate practice. This concept separates the elite coach from the rest of the pack.

The strength coach can support performance

There are three special tools the strength coach can use to support and improve performance on the field of play:

- ◆ Appropriate heart rate
- ◆ Appropriate physical tension and relaxation
- ◆ Appropriate arousal

The head coach and the strength coach should work seamlessly. Now, in this fantasy world I just envisioned, this is ideal.

I constantly explain the plight of the strength coach to people like this:

"Last hired. First fired."

If a player drops the ball on the most important play of the season, someone will trace it back to a deadlift session five months ago.

"Ah, too many deadlifts!"

Since few understand the role of weights and the weightroom, the strength coach is always a convenient target for blame.

Years ago, we lost a game where two players contributed seven turnovers combined. In American football, more than three will doom a victory. The athletes told the coaches they were exhausted from lifting that week. The coaches believed it.

Their attendance records for that week indicated they both skipped the weight classes for the two weeks going into that game. And, because they were star football players, no discipline was handed out.

So: The head coach and the strength coach should work seamlessly.

When it's done well, amazing things can happen. Often, in some sports like track and field or swimming or wrestling, the coaching staff run both the technical practices and the conditioning work in the arena and the weightroom. Generally, these situations tend to produce a balanced athlete. Moreover, the coaching staff sees and knows the gaps between practice and performance without having to have a meeting.

In other words, the athlete can't complain about one coach to another…it's the same person!

And, if you can do it as a coach, this is a good situation. Division I American football coaches are beginning to pay huge salaries to the strength coaches. These head coaches have discovered, like elite rugby teams did, that strength and conditioning are key to victory in collision sports.

It's true in most everything else, too.

Coaching performance: The goal is to keep the goal the goal

When I first started doing workshops, people would giggle when I said, "The goal is to keep the goal the goal." It later became a catchphrase for every workshop, article and book I deliver. It's the secret to good coaching and outstanding performance.

Originally, the phrase was, "The mission is to keep the mission the mission." It might be passé now, but two decades ago, many success workshops focused on finding a mission statement. There were perils in not finding one, and many companies have vanished because they misunderstood this key.

If you prided yourself in making the finest buggy whips, things are fine until the car replaces the horse-drawn carriage. One company, a big name, thought print photos would be around forever. Well, maybe that's true…but digital devices and social media made them relics, and the company died.

If the buggy-whip company decided to be the best at mobile accessories, they might still be around.

But, there's more—something that's often referred to as "mission creep."

We have seen it in most areas of life. The U. S. Marine Corps master running into the teeth of conflict. Asking them to teach preschool at a refugee camp is mission creep. Most of us know athletes who decide to really bulk up or lean down, and go on to lose a season dealing with issues of too much or too little lean body mass.

You can't be a Highland Games heavy athlete and worry about having six-pack abs. If you choose to be in a physique contest, it might not be a good time to plan a wedding at the same time (trust me). In other words, if you chase two rabbits, you go home hungry.

Most of us go hungry when it comes to achieving goals and successes because we chase a rabbit until we see a squirrel and then...wait, what?

Squirrel?

The goal is to keep the goal the goal.

Certainly, the realities of genetics, opponents and luck (yes, luck is a reality that might need a better word, but it's part of performance) may cause you to adapt your goal or even ratchet it down, but, for the most part, keep focused on the goal.

The *Gnolls Credo* and fighter pilots

I have the opportunity to travel a lot. Sometimes, when I come to a city, I really want to see just one thing:

+ 221B Baker Street (the taxi driver told me, "I've never heard of Sherlock Holmes")
+ The Vietnam War Memorial
+ Stones

It's that third one that might throw you. Throughout Ireland there are burial tombs and ring forts and, frankly, stones littered throughout the land that were placed by people just like us long before the Pharaohs demanded their pyramids to be built. I wanted to rub my hands on these stones and connect back to the poets, saints and sinners who had walked past them before me.

Adrian Cradock, my former intern and now one of the most sought-out trainers in Ireland, took us up to County Sligo on a recent trip. His brother's wife's brother, Christopher Taylor, offered to take us on a hike among the stones. The entire western coast of Ireland is one large historical site and archeological dig.

It was amazing, of course, but, as is the norm, the conversation was just as good. He asked if I had read J. Stanton's book, *The Gnolls Credo.*

The what?

The gnolls are half-human and half-hyena and, yes, I just typed that phrase. There are dozens of great takeaways from the book, but the best is the following set of rules:

+ Plan the hunt
+ Hunt
+ Discuss the hunt

If you ask me for the number-one problem in the fitness field, my response would reflect this list: Our collective inability to focus and finish any diet plan or training program makes us constantly planning and discussing and missing the key point.

Hunt.

In other words, any stupid thing you want to do is fine. Just do it. (I just invented that phrase.) Twelve weeks of this or that… fine. Just finish it, and then we can talk about it. As I have noted countless times: Every diet works, every training program works, but you have to finish the thing.

Then we can discuss it.

But we don't. The joke in fitness is that the very best diet or training plan you will ever do is the next one.

If I could, I would sentence everyone to a term in training and diet jail until they finish every great new idea. Then, please, move on to something fresh, new and exciting, but finish the plan.

- Plan the hunt
- Hunt
- Discuss the hunt

And, in that order!

For a principle-based coaching system—and who in their right minds would do anything else?—we can add a little corollary to Stanton's Gnolls Credo:

- Plan the hunt *(These are the principles; let's do them.)*
- Hunt *(Do them!)*
- Discuss the hunt *(Did we achieve the principles?)*

A follow-up and ongoing question: Were these the best principles?

Oddly, I know this is true. I can't imagine a better principle for throwers than "Throw far." For American football, "Block, tackle and fall on the ball" have been true since the first time two college teams took a whack at each other.

General Kurt Neubauer took me aside after a recent talk and told me this is exactly what every fighter-pilot group does before every flight. For the record: EVERY flight. There are no joy rides on multi-million-dollar supersonic armored arrows. Their Gnolls Credo is this:

- Brief the objectives
- Mission
- Debrief the objectives

And, as we saw earlier, they apply the "Five Whys" matrix: Two questions:

- Kill?
- Survive?

Then they do the five "whys" if either answer is "No."

From here, we need to find a solution to the last "why." This is practicing appropriately.

Practicing appropriately

Practicing appropriately in the world of any kind of performance is simple: What are the principles we are trying to achieve—to focus on first and foremost? Now, how do we apply performance pressures, problems and situations to our practice sessions?

If these are the principles and we set up practice scenarios that reflect the stresses of our competition or mission, we then assess our practices with the "Five Whys" matrix.

- The principles need to be determined first.
- Appropriate practice comes next.
- The "Five Whys" matrix must be applied after practices.

How do we make practice more appropriate? It's not necessarily going to be harder.

But, it *is* going to be smarter.

The study that changed my life

Years ago, I would take a monthly journey up the hill to the University of Utah library and catch up on journals and quarterlies. Now, most of the magazines had almost no carryover, but *Track and Field Quarterly* and *Soviet Sports Review* always had something I could apply to training, either my own or that of my athletes.

I always tried to read these with a grain of salt. For example, John Powell told me his 550-pound bench press as reported in *Soviet Sports Review* never happened and he thinks that was just some coach's attempt to get his athletes in the weightroom more. I also knew many of the training programs were missing discussions of pills and syringes that were and remain a major part of many systems' training programs.

But I always learned. A phrase to teach or a drill or even a piece of exercise equipment would sneak into our training, and, sometimes, like kettlebells, they worked better than I hoped.

One study bumped around inside my head for a long time: The Soviets were discovering that many of their soccer players were outstanding in drills but could not perform at the same level in games. Instead of calling these athletes tags like "scrimmage heroes" or "chokes," the coaches dug deeper. Using heart-rate monitors, they discovered a simple thing:

> *In the drills, the heart rates were in the low 90s. In games, heart rates varied from 155 to 185.*

Doing something at 90 beats per minute is *nothing* like doing the same thing at double the heart pounding. Later, I mentioned this to a famous soccer coach, who told me a simple thing to watch out for with a tired player:

> *"When they 'head' the ball, it goes up."*

Wait…what?

When fresh, the athletes leap up and drive the ball down. A tired athlete gets under the ball, and it pops up. As always, coaching and science seem to walk together.

Most coaches discover some kind of wisdom when it comes to conditioning for sports. True, enough is enough in conditioning, but it has to be there when demanded. In basketball, "free throws when tired" is not only a key to victory—it's also a conditioning recipe.

That study changed my thinking.

Recently, at a workshop, a young lady asked all of the speakers to define "fitness." I was a little surprised how those who focus on personal training tended to get "fitness"—the ability to do a task—muddled with "performance."

Performance—that instant your name gets called under the lights and you need to strike the spark—is different.

The Soviet soccer study opened my eyes about appropriate training. Yes, we need to do some things tired. But, this was only the beginning of my journey into understanding appropriate practice.

Appropriate heart rate started the journey. Then, reading some work with World War II fighter pilots carried me deeper into this when they discovered they had a hard time closing their eyes to sleep.

With the body under some control, we are finally ready to deal with appropriate mental stimulation: the arousal levels.

It's not choking!

I hate the word "choke" when referring to athletic performance. I'm not asking to lie down on the therapist's table, but in my youth I was under a lot of personal and social pressure. When I threw 160 feet for the first time, I was asked when I would crush the 170-foot barrier.

If I threw a personal best, I was expected to top it each and every week, regardless of weather or conditions. I had coaches walk away during my bad performances and people tell me I choked after, in hindsight, some fairly good competitive efforts.

Dick Notmeyer saved me. He was the consummate storyteller and understood that I needed to ease off the dial of physical tension and mental arousal. I needed, in his words, a "tranquil mind." He developed this in me through role playing in training and constant storytelling about other athletes who rose to the top.

My career success is based on Dick's simple, intuitive methods.

It's not choking when an athlete performs poorly; it's a lack of appropriate practice. Let's fix that.

First, what do we need to practice?

At first glance, "what do we need to practice?" seems obvious. To summarize good coaching:

> *Swimmers swim.*
>
> *Jumpers jump.*
>
> *Throwers throw.*
>
> *Kickers kick.*

And, I can go on. The devil, as always, is in the details. There is no question that swimmers should swim, but what is the focus of training? More swimming? Swim 24 hours a day?

I have a simple mental exercise for training clarity: If, for whatever reason, you were allowed only three 15-minute sessions a week to train for your goal (imagine you are a political prisoner for being too kind and helpful), what would you do?

I call this exercise the "Prisoner's Dilemma."

As a discus thrower, I would grab a six-pound powerball and do full turns into a wall so the implement would just fall straight down and I could do a lot of reps. I might have a barbell close by for some snatches and overhead squats, and a kettlebell for swings, presses and goblet squats.

I just gave you the template for training a discus thrower:

- ◆ Lots of full-turn throws
- ◆ Some lifting

If you come to my practice and see hours of yoga, jogging and dodgeball, feel free to whack me on the head. I'm probably brain dead already if I'm doing that kind of stuff as a thrower.

Now, there is nothing wrong with yoga, jogging and dodgeball, but you can expect to see my throwers throwing a lot and lifting.

I ask this same question another way: What are the three… and only three…keys to success in your field? Generally, the conclusions are the same as the Prisoner's Dilemma. I love asking this question, as it sparks a great discussion afterwards.

Fighter pilot:

> *"Speed is life"*
>
> *"Hit and run"*
>
> *"Straight lines, small hooks" (I had to follow up on this. Basically, it means go fast and straight and don't turn much.)*

Famous basketball coach:

> *"Offensive rebounds"*
>
> *"Transition defense"*
>
> *"Free throws when tired"*

My knowledge of basketball is limited, but the coach's head nodded up and down as he stared off into space remembering details of past losses.

Josh Hillis on fat loss:

> *"Food prep"*
>
> *"Food journal"*
>
> *"Get stronger"*

What cliché do you want to work with? The Big Rocks? Pareto's Law? Most of us know the basic principle here: In every endeavor, there are a few big keys. Focusing your energy on them will save you a lot of time.

The big rocks story

A teacher walks into a classroom and sets a glass jar on the table. He silently places two-inch rocks in the jar until no more can fit. He asks the class if the jar is full and they agree it is.

He says, "Really," and pulls out a pile of small pebbles, adding them to the jar, shaking it slightly until they fill the spaces between the rocks. He asks again, "Is the jar full?" They agree.

So next, he adds a scoop of sand to the jar, filling the space between the pebbles and asks the question again. This time, the class is divided, some feeling that the jar is obviously full, but others are wary of another trick.

So he grabs a pitcher of water and fills the jar to the brim, saying, "If this jar is your life, what does this experiment show you?"

A bold student replies, "No matter how busy you think you are, you can always take on more."

"That is one view," he replies.

Then he looks out at the class, making eye contact with everyone, "The rocks represent the BIG *things in your life—what you will value at the end of your life—your family, your partner, your health, fulfilling your hopes and dreams. The pebbles are the other things in your life that give it meaning, like your job, your house, your hobbies, your friendships. The sand and water represent the 'small stuff' that fills our time, like watching* TV *or running errands."*

Looking out at the class again, he asks, "Can you see what would happen if I started with the sand or the pebbles?"

From *Storlietelling.com,* see http://bit.ly/1nQKeQe

Pareto

The Pareto Principle is the idea that, for most things, roughly 80% of the effects come from 20% of the causes. The Italian economist Vilfredo Pareto published a paper in 1896, *Cours d'économie Politique.* Pareto developed the principle by observing that 20% of the peapods in his garden contained 80% of the peas. If tweets still exist when you read this: 80% of the tweets are made by 20% of the people doing the tweeting.

The Prisoner's Dilemma and Pareto's Law give you the big rocks and the 20%.

Yes, everything is important. But, everything else is not *as important* as the big rocks and the 20%. That's why elite coaches emphasize the basics, the fundamentals.

To find the basics, take a few minutes to minimize everything into what is the *least* you can do to be successful.

Then, train that with every ounce of energy you can find.

Once you find your three keys, the big rocks and the 20%, focus on what John T. Reed reminds us: "Correct the correctable."

As a basketball coach, you can emphasize offensive rebounds by working on drills, positioning and opponents' tendencies. You can't ask for taller athletes. Correct the correctable!

Good coaching walks the path between "This is important" and "This is what we have to work with." Both are important and true. When you start wishing for seven-footers or faster kids, you are no longer coaching.

Neil Gaiman said it best in *MirrorMask:*

"We often confuse what we wish for with what is."

Coach what is.

- Find the 20% that provides the 80%.
- Find the three keys.
- Find the answer to the Prisoner's Dilemma.
- Correct the correctable.
- Then, match some of the training to the appropriate heart rate, arousal and tension.

Chapter 8

Tension, Arousal and Relaxation

PHYSICAL TENSION CAN IMPROVE performance. Physical tension can also destroy performance. Tension is a dosage issue: Like Goldilocks, we have to search for "just right."

In Dr. Bob Ward's *Building the Perfect Star: Changing the Trajectory of Sports and the People in Them* (a book about Dallas Cowboys football), he has a great insight: What is the quickest way to get an athlete to run at 85%?

"Get 'em to think!"

When it comes to tension, we can use the brain to *think* its way to more tension when appropriate or less tension when appropriate.

But tension offers more: It's one of the ultimate teaching tools for technique.

Master skill: appropriate tension levels

Let's start with the extremes. There are times when maximal tension can improve performance. This would be most obvious in the three powerlifts—the squat, the bench press and the deadlift. Tension literally holds the body together under maximal loads. Injuries—terrible injuries—can occur in powerlifting in an instant of tension loss.

The plank family teaches tension. In the 1-2-3-4 Assessment from *Can You Go?* we test strength with the two-minute plank test. Yes, we get some clues into overall core strength and the ability to pack the shoulders, but we are actually testing the ability to hold tension over time.

Teaching tension to a young lifter is part of the foundation of building strength. To press heavy loads overhead, the lifter must grab the ground with the feet, squeeze every muscle in the lower body, maintain a boa-like constriction on the thoracic area and drive the bar overhead.

Planks teach tension. For the push family, and as an introduction to the basic concept, use planks, pushup position planks

(PUPPs), handstand variations and cartwheels. Cartwheels are moving planks…an oxymoron, but true.

For pulls, squeezing the contracted position in rows or pull-ups, where the bar is at your neck, practices tension. In addition, hanging from bars and rings seems to help teach methods of tension.

Isometric hinges are marvelous. The king of this goes by many names: hip thrust, pelvic tilt and supine bridges. These are also marvelous for teaching the hinge, that fundamental movement of kettlebells and the Olympic lifts.

The goblet squat, I argue, is another moving plank. With the weight held in front of the body without support, the person needs to constantly counter—plank—the load through the positions.

The loaded carries teach integrity under load. These exercises teach the body to remain as one piece as we move forward. The suitcase carry—walks with the load in only in one hand—are especially excellent for teaching this principle of tension during movement.

High tension

The powerlifts reward high tension. They also clue us in to the emotional impact of training. The best example I can give is of my daughter, Kelly. She is blonde, blue-eyed and barely over five feet. But it's five feet of attitude.

I have learned that 275 pounds is the line in the sand for female high school athletes. When they deadlift 275, no matter their weight, height or build, good things happen on the field of play.

The first time Kelly pulled the weight, it popped off the floor and she locked it out. She released the bar and began sobbing.

There's no crying in the weightroom.

I ran over, thinking I had an injured athlete.

"What's wrong? Hurt? Where?"

"I'm fine. I'm just crying."

It took me years to figure this out.

Most of us walk through life at a tension level of about five. I have this dial in my head when it comes to this kind of thing: One is the lowest and 10 is when you stick your finger in the outlet and your hair fries. A few boozy drinks at night might take some of the edge off after work, but a peek at work email might lead to a lousy night's sleep. Single moms probably live at six or seven.

A max deadlift rails you up to a 10. BANG! Release the bar and...and...I'm fine, I'm just crying. Unloading all that tension leads to an emotional upheaval.

Sobbing is rare, but many of us know how lifting and dropping weights can bring clarity to a crappy day.

Tension not only teaches the body to build the structure to support heavy lifts; tension can also teach technique.

Done correctly, tension teaches technique.

Isometrics

Isometrics, also known as functional isometric contraction, hit a wave of popularity in the early 1960s. Studies on frogs showed that strength could be improved in squeezing out short bursts of absolute contraction in a muscle—generally the number was about 10 seconds. The poor frogs were held down and prodded with electrodes.

Science!

Soon, the Olympic lifting world discovered isometrics, along with the first steroids, and everybody was pushing and pulling and squatting door jams, chairs and brick walls. The fad quickly tired after people came up short without the magic of the pink pills.

Years later, I interviewed Dick Smith, who was in a front-row seat for the whole isometrics show. Money ruined everything, he told me. Bob Hoffman, the owner of York Barbell, wanted to sell isometric racks.

Dick told me that few even tried to understand the technique. Isometrics are exhausting but don't *seem* to be because, to quote, "You don't move." It's hard to argue with that. Moreover, Dick noted that the greatness of the idea was in working the weak points, but first you had to find them.

I had been struggling for years to rise out of my competition clean and jerks. Dave Turner, my lifting coach, eyed the exact mark where I struggled and we measured the position. It was 34 inches off the ground. For six weeks, I set the rack at 34 inches, squeezed under a loaded bar and tried to stand up.

Week one, I was struggling with 135. At the end of week six, I stood up with 365 pounds from my weak spot and never missed standing up from another clean the rest of my career.

Isometrics teach tension. Isometrics work on weak spots. And, isometrics can teach technique.

As the electrified frogs taught us, isometrics build strength. But, also in those six weeks, I learned the position. My body "found" the leverages. I learned how to be not only comfortable there, but to explode from that position.

Tension can be used to teach technique!

There's a position in all throwing sports where the implement is opposite the throwing target, called the sector. Often, mastering the patience to find that position and applying the "bow and arrow" forces separates the good from the bad efforts.

I have my athletes get into *that* position and squeeze and tighten every muscle of the body. It helps to hold onto something that won't move...like a building. Squeeze everything and hold it. I then ask them to "dial down" the tension by shaking out, and then we complete a full throw.

More often than not, the eyes of the athlete light up.

"That's it…there!"

If you can't find a position fast, you have to slow down. Nothing is slower than not moving.

My approach to coaching changed when I read a post by Jason F. Keen highlighting a $51 workshop he attended in Minnesota. I printed it out on May 2, 2000, because back then, I figured nothing would stick around on the internet.

Now, I know better: Good information vanishes overnight on the 'net, but that one drunken butt-cheek photo has a life of its own.

Jason gave an overview of a talk by Pavel Tsatsouline. At the time, Pavel was making a name for himself in Minnesota and soon, with John Du Cane, would change the lifting world with the reintroduction of kettlebells.

"The basic premise Pavel holds dear is *strength equals tension*. We need to learn to *not* contract as fast as possible, but to learn to contract as *hard* as possible."

Jason went on to describe the methods of hyperirridation, this practice of consciously squeezing every muscle, from the toes, through the legs, the core and to the opposite arm to press or curl a weight.

Strength equals tension

The best way to teach tension is with isometrics and planks. These are the roots of any good training system.

Tension also addresses issues. When doing kettlebell swings, one of the most dynamic moves a human can do (when done correctly!), errors are difficult to fix. It's like trying to fix a side mirror, by hand, flying down the freeway at 85 miles an hour. Every time you reach out the window, juggle the side mirror and then sit back to see if it's right, you risk barreling into the neighboring lane.

It's best to pull over and stop.

With poor swing technique, it's also best to pull over and stop.

Two glaring errors show up in most people's kettlebell swing: At the top—the position with the body straight, the 'bell horizontal to the floor, and the body fighting (planking) to hold that position—people tend to make two errors:

♦ Soften the belly
♦ Raise the shoulders

Both can be cured by a simple drill that has become part of our basic tools, as it simplifies the teaching process.

Hop to the floor in the hip-thrust position. Squeeze your butt cheeks and drive your hips to the sky. Hold. Feel the level of tension in the glutes. Relax and repeat. This time, add crossing your hands and pointing to vertical. Have a partner apply pressure…a lot…to your palms, and then try to pull your hands to your knees.

As you do, the abs will contract like crazy. When this happens, the glutes will clench more, too. You will also notice the shoulders slide into the "packed" position, the safe place for shoulders to be for shoulder happiness.

If the student is good, let's pop up and fire off a few kettlebell swings. Strive for the same level of tension as was felt in the isometric drill. Usually, this is the cure.

Tension is the master teacher. Tension teaches strength. Tension teaches technique.

The concepts of tension and relaxation, like so many things, go together like yin and yang. I might overuse that symbol concept at times, but it works well in coaching, and I think I'll keep using it.

Tension needs to be taught—relaxation needs to be taught

The work of Bud Winters changed my life. Bud was the track coach at San Jose State and also worked with fighter pilots during WWII. It was during his time coaching fighter pilots that he came up with an insight about much of life: *Relax and win.*

Teaching fighter pilots to relax allowed them to improve on every test and every skill, including recognizing friend from foe. He took these insights into athletics and the world has never seen a better track team than his. His athletes once held *every* world record up to 800 meters (in every conceivable variation); his pole vaulter was the first over 18 feet, and he had champions in the throws, including John Powell.

The system, called *Relax and Win,* worked. It was based on some very simple concepts:

1. You can learn to relax.

2. Teach yourself to get to sleep quickly and easily (the master recovery tool).

3. There is a value in hypnosis.

4. Understand the importance of mental set, what would later become "affirmations."

5. Use physical warmups to provide relaxation.

6. Humor, vigorous shaking and swinging of the limbs induce relaxation.

The book *Relax and Win* is again in publication. For the modern athlete and coach, nothing in the book is groundbreaking, as you may have heard it all.

And, that makes sense because Bud Winters is the guy who broke the ground!

I recommend athletes have a sleep ritual, including blue light-blocking glasses, dark and cool bedrooms and a soak in a hot tub or a shower before bed. Mastery of sleeping seems to be a first step in building a better performance. General warming up—not actual competitive practice—seems to loosen up not only the athlete, but also the athlete's mind.

Controlling the tension dial is a key to all sports. There are some sports, like powerlifting, that you need the dial at nine out of 10. The more tension you have, the better your performance.

Discus throwing needs a four. Smile as you throw. Shot putting needs more...you can snarl if you wish.

That's why I think discus throwers get so much from the Olympic snatch: It's more like a four on the tension dial. The clean and jerk demands more physical tension, and that helps the shot putter.

During practice, consciously raise and lower physical tension. Wear extra clothes, warm up longer, laugh a lot and get as loose as you can. Assess. Did that help performance?

If the answer is "Yes," excellent. You may have discovered the right physical-tension level for your event. If the answer is "No," add tension. Try planking or deadlifting or squeezing into isometrics.

Again, assess. Keep moving the dial up and down until you find the appropriate physical tension level. Under the pressures of performance, the athlete needs a tool kit to raise physical tension (sometimes) or lower it (more often).

Here is a quick checklist to lowering tension. Laminate this and put it in your gym bag:

1. Fast and loose drills from Bud Winters

    a. Shake it out
    b. Wiggle the jaw
    c. Smile

2. Breath control—counting is the simplest

3. Heat

If you need to raise tension (this is a bit more unusual for most people):

    a. Planks
    b. Isometrics
    c. Cold

"Psyching *up*" seems to be something you don't see much, but powerlifters and shot putters might need it. This is rare, but possible.

In practice, try these methods, then debrief the mission. This is a skill that needs to be practiced.

Appropriately!

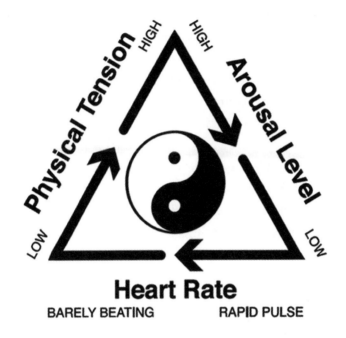

Master skill: appropriate arousal levels

Bud Winters proved that physical relaxation helped fighter pilots and track-and-field athletes. But we can take this farther.

Physical relaxation leads to mental relaxation.

So, arousal is something that needs to be considered and trained long before the event.

Usually when I teach this to young athletes, I hear a snicker at "arousal." I'm fine with that. Yes, the word is also used in sexual interactions.

Let me say this as appropriately as I can: Appropriate arousal makes sexual relationships "work," if you understand the point—for both genders. If you don't understand this, it might be a worthy conversation topic with that other person.

Arousal in athletics is a master skill.

Al Oerter, the four-time Olympic discus champion, told someone, "Long warmups are poison!" I have heard this story from two different people who claim to be the someone.

Warmups can have a great value in establishing the right tension, arousal and heart-rate levels. They are also free of much of the stress. In throwing, having a great warmup throw raises the expectations of the day…it raises the arousal.

When the reality of the meet sets in and one's name is called, *too much* excitement, enthusiasm and arousal destroys the timing of a proper throw.

The *right amount* of arousal is the key.

We can train the physical-tension knob with appropriate practice and choice of lifts. With arousal, we need to take this a step farther. We need to actively have more arousal in training than we do in competition.

Let me share three ideas:

1. One-throw competitions

2. Trading conditioning drills for successful completion of a task

3. Practicing switching it on and off

I have discussed the idea of one-throw competitions many times. At a track meet, we get up to six throws. At a practice session, I might circle a day and tell everybody, "One-throw comp next Friday at 4:00."

The athletes get one throw. They can warm up, practice, drink their magic sauce and sprinkle lucky charms all over the ring. Everyone then gets one throw; we measure and—this is really important—post the results. My best-ever thrower hated this so much, he ripped the results off the wall and left the staples.

This teaches arousal. It doesn't sound like much, but cutting the number of allowed throws makes the athlete have to perform *now*. Rarely in life or sport do we get second chances, and this teaches the athlete to quickly get into the zone and find the edge or groove.

It shouldn't surprise anyone that throwers win a lot of meets on the last throw, the first throw or in "do or die" situations. We have trained that into them.

As an athlete matures, we should add more stress. I'll have an athlete stand up and then immediately sit back down. I yell about stupid stuff (my athletes tell me I'm not good at trying to rattle them) and even stop them mid-performance. It might take 45 minutes of useless badgering and cajoling before I allow them to throw.

The athletes might be laughing or smiling, but the arousal work is still going on.

Arousal levels in sport

Trading conditioning is a fun thing to do. There is a drill called "The Miami Drill" that I think I got from Jimmy Johnson, the former coach of the Miami Hurricanes. It's 10 100-yard sprints with 30 seconds rest between each run.

It probably has little actual value, in all honesty. So, after number three, I might stop the drill and yell, "Field goal team! Get on the 35-yard line. If you make it, we don't do any more sprints!"

Now, you can do this with any team sport, but note: We're teaching something important here—football games come down to successful field goals at the end of the game. The arousal level of the field goal unit is very high, knowing that the entire program's heart and lungs are hoping you make the kick.

Trust me, the snapper, holder and kicker are going to be taking practice much more seriously after this opportunity.

As in a game, this unit can be the heroes or the goats. This is the best way I know to get the feel of a game without filling the stands with people.

"Practicing switching it on and off" is a master technique.

A few years ago, we had a wedding with a Highland Games as part of the reception. This, by the way, is an awesome idea! Friends marveled at the ability of the athletes to switch the focus and arousal from holding champagne to picking up a caber. I think the strength sports teach this well: There's a real chance you can get badly injured in training doing the Olympic lifts or the powerlifts. You need to be in the right range of focus and arousal for each and every lift.

But, you can't stay like that for hours. You have to switch it on and off.

In collision sports and occupations, you need both wide and narrow focus as things develop. When the other team breaks the huddle, you need wide focus and low arousal. As the running back comes at you, the focus should narrow and the arousal should rise some.

Turning arousal up and down is a skill that allows you to sleep before competition, to digest well, eliminate at the appropriate time, and perform when it's time to perform.

Apply arousal practice.

Then, take the advice of General Neubauer and:

+ Brief the objectives
+ Mission
+ Debrief the objectives

I run these drills almost entirely through the principle that dictates our performance goal. Did the athlete throw far? The debriefing is pretty simple: yes or no. If the answer is "No," this athlete might need more work on fine-tuning arousal levels. Simply lifting more or training harder won't overcome an issue with arousal levels.

I still believe Bud Winter's *Relax and Win* methods are the best way to get the arousal levels under control. As most adults in the real world will tell you, too much and constant tension leads to issues. This chart is what I use to explain the two most common ways of discussing stress: sympathetic and parasympathetic.

Sympathetic-system dominant

Fight or flight

We need to relax

Reduce intensity

Hot tub, lighter diet

Do some mobility and flexibility

Parasympathetic-system dominant

Rest and digest

We to need to stimulate the system

We can ramp things up

Ice showers, more protein

Let's wake up the system

Arousal control and dialing up and down physical tension teach the athlete a toolkit to help swim through these two systems. There isn't a good or bad here—this isn't moral theology—and both are important for success.

Master skill: appropriate heart rate

Physical-tension and relaxation drills and arousal-control drills can do a lot to improve performance. The third master skill is appropriate heart rate.

This becomes easier if you have tension and arousal already dialed in. At a track meet, you might find elite athletes with a huge range of appropriate heart-rate numbers. What defines appropriate heart rate might be the ultimate "it depends" answer. A javelin thrower might be grooving technique with a pulse well under 100 beats per minute. The male 400-meter runner just finishing the race might be pounding a hole in his chest.

It depends!

Let's make this simple.

The easy part:

If it's too low, jump around, whip your arms, move—I think you know what to do!

The hard one:

Too high! Breathing drills, calming drills, catching your breath, resting—all easy to write in this nice, warm room where I'm typing.

Learning to slow your heart rate during performance takes practice. It's hard to tell your heart to slow down under high tension, high arousal, 126,000 fans cheering and the team on attack. Getting the heart rate down, under pressure, is a master technique. Getting the heart rate to slow down under pressure is well worth the time in training.

Be sure to test various heart rates in training, and then debrief the experience.

Applying tension, arousal and heart-rate control to principles

Using this approach is illuminating. If you have principles (either handed down in the coaching tradition or discovered through the Prisoner's Dilemma or the three keys discussion—see page 129 for a reminder), you can run through a whole training matrix based on testing and debriefing the application of tension, arousal and heart-rate control.

Let's look at two examples.

Basketball

Free throws when tired

1. Heart rate?
2. Tension and relaxation?
3. Arousal scale?

Transitional defense

1. Heart rate?
2. Tension and relaxation?
3. Arousal scale?

Offensive rebounds

1. Heart rate?
2. Tension and relaxation?
3. Arousal scale?

I can see clearly—and I truly know little about basketball—that the arousal needed for offensive rebounds would be higher than free throws when tired. These athletes need arousal-control efforts to raise and lower this quality almost instantly.

Heart rate would seem to be a crucial area for basketball success. I'm sure there would be a value in charting heart rate through game situations to get a handle on this and then determine appropriate practice techniques.

For the hurdles in track and field

It's *10 hurdles* (not 1-2-3)

1. Heart rate?
2. Tension and relaxation?
3. Arousal scale?

Attack with the lead knee

1. Heart rate?
2. Tension and relaxation?
3. Arousal scale?

It's the *10th hurdle*

1. Heart rate?
2. Tension and relaxation?
3. Arousal scale?

At a glance, we can see the need for heart-rate training at the end of the race. If the hurdler trains technique at a lower heart rate and finds it leaps up approaching the 10th hurdle, the technical-training issue resurfaces from the Soviet soccer study.

It comes down to this: When training for high performance, it does little good to have sessions filled with light comedy, dodgeball and general idiocy, unless, of course, that is the sport.

You must strive to match the demands of high performance in the practice sessions.

And that is practicing appropriately.

The dusty corners

The "practice appropriately" training model has three corners:

+ Low tension (high relaxation) and low heart rate
+ High tension and high arousal
+ High heart rate and low arousal

These might be something like:

- ◆ Sleep, good food, hot tub
- ◆ Powerlifting, planks, presses
- ◆ Traditional mindless cardio work

You know, that's not bad.

In fact, it's pretty good.

This is probably the way most athletes have trained since lifting became part of the training scene. You will certainly find elite athletes—gifted elite athletes—who can thrive on treadmills, some lifting and fast food!

For the rest of us mortals, we need to match the training with our performance needs. But, the dusty corners deserve some study. Marty Gallagher focuses on this with his athletes. To sum Marty's ideas (never a great idea):

1. 12-week linear periodization
2. Wholesome food
3. Third-way cardio (exercises like HeavyHands or combining upper and lower body for cardiovascular training)

One thing missing here, of course, is Marty's constant focus on *perfect* technique. I hate to call his training the "dusty corners," but for powerlifting, it's the right recipe.

This is my concern about having powerlifters or former Special Forces people coaching strength and conditioning. They have a lot to offer, but they still need to properly apply their ideas to the performance of the sport.

As the saying goes, "If all you have is a hammer, the whole world is nails."

Expand the toolbox.

Performance is about taking first. Winning! A coach needs to spend a lot of time insuring that practice elevates the performer to elite levels.

The elite athlete must master this point:

"Performance trumps practice."

From there, focus on training that will give the biggest bang for the buck. The athlete must train appropriately with the principles of the sport.

Chapter 9

Training Elite Athletes

IN ORDER TO TRANSITION FROM simply saying "practice appropriately" to applying these principles for an elite athlete, we need a moment to focus on one question:

What is an elite athlete or performer?

Everyone thinks they are special—even elite. Everybody wants to put a bumper sticker on the cars because little Billy was the school's honor student. But elite athletes tend to reflect these points:

1. The athlete is no longer on a steep learning curve. The athlete is no longer improving in quantum leaps from year to year or season to season. Lifts, for example, no longer double over two years. Improvement is slow.

2. The athlete has a year-round approach to one sport.

3. The athlete uses some form of intense training camp or focused training each year.

4. The athlete uses high levels of strength training before the competitive periods. Save for lifters, as strength levels go down, performance should improve.

5. The athlete has made a personal choice to be elite.

Let's look at each point and widen our view about elite.

Point one—The athlete is no longer on a steep learning curve. The athlete is no longer improving in quantum leaps from year to year or season to season. Lifts, for example, no longer double over two years. Improvement is slow.

The first point is hard for many to understand because it also has an interesting corollary. A few years ago at dinner, Yuri Sedych, still the world record holder in the hammer (and it's been a long, long time since he set it), told me a simple definition of elite.

He leaned in, checked the room for eavesdroppers like a good Comrade should, and told me, "If you improve every year, you are elite."

I know that holding conflicting concepts in your head can damage your brain. So here it is: You are no longer improving by leaps and bounds, but at the same time, you are still improving.

Both John Powell and Tommy Kono made one final point that I can never emphasize enough:

> *Once you choose a sport, if you are not elite in two or three years, you are simply not good enough to be on the path to elite.*

No, that is not nice, but it is true.

Point two—The athlete has a year-round approach to one sport.

I made quite a career of wearing a kilt one weekend and a singlet the next. I always maintained that the cross training of Olympic lifting and Highland Games would make me a better discus thrower. I was wrong.

It pains me to say it.

Highland Games gave me a limp, and O lifting blew my left wrist into enough pieces to warrant two surgeries. When I give workshops today, I often caution people to follow Andrew Carnegie's advice:

> *"Put all your eggs in one basket...and carefully watch that basket!"*

True, there is a time and place for "all of this." You should know that in basketball you can score one, two or three points depending on what is going on in the game and where you're standing or jumping from. But, if you're a high jumper and you blow your ankle out playing basketball before the Nationals, your career is over (and, yes, Calvin, I am talking about you).

Now, it's fine to take a month, six weeks or two months away from your focus to try other things, but the bulk of your time, energy and attention needs to be on that one basket of eggs!

Point three—The athlete uses some form of intense training camp or focused training each year.

A great memory of my life was meeting a legendary body-builder, Robby Robinson. He came up to me while I was doing power cleans in the corner of the original Gold's Gym and told me I was on the right track. Even though I was a discus thrower,

I still thought it was worth my time to spend several days in Santa Monica to see what was going on during the renaissance of bodybuilding that was happening in the mid-1970s.

I go to discus camps and usually learn more about things like sleds, kettlebells, hill runs, slosh pipes, chains, nutrition and caber tossing than I do about the discus. If you go to a clinic with a bodybuilder, you tend to hear a lot of insights about learning to starve and about recovery—"There is no overtraining; there is only under-recovery" is a great quote from one such workshop.

I've said this before: Get out of the comfy confines of your local spa and go see what the best are doing. Go to a clinic. Take a certification course. Find out what is really going on. Get your hands dirty and relearn the basics—or maybe learn them for the first time. If there isn't a formal camp to go to, book a hotel room near a gym or a place you need to train and go there and immerse yourself in the place.

Point four—The athlete uses high levels of strength training before the competitive periods. Save for lifters, as strength levels go down, performance should improve.

I learned this insight years ago from John Powell. The explanation was so simple I nearly cried:

> *The body, especially the nervous system, can be asked to do only so many things at once.*

In other words, get as strong as you can. *Then* work on the other qualities you need.

Point five—The athlete has made a personal choice to be elite.

I have written about goal setting time and time again. In fact, see Appendix Three on page 235 for a lengthy recap. Many people wash over these articles with a blank look and ignore the importance. It comes down to this: If athletes want to be great—the best, the king of the hill, number one, top of the list—they need to *make the choice* to do it.

They might have the genetics to do it, but natural talent gets us only so far.

Your athletes might have a mom or dad pushing kids into sports, but in my experience working with some of my athletes, this can be a millstone around their necks.

We make this choice by setting goals.

If you want to get extremely low numbers on your bodyfat tests, you are going to have to push away and push aside temptations in the form of sweets and fatty goo nearly every day, if not nearly every hour. This can't be done by anyone else, not over the long term.

You have to have courage in reserve to achieve great goals.

But, *you* have to have it. No one can do it for you. And you can't do it for your athletes.

And, while it's fresh in my mind, what makes an elite coach?

What is an elite coach?

1. *The elite coach understands cost-to-benefit ratios.*

2. *The elite coach understands that enough is enough.*

3. *The elite coach knows to correct the correctable.*

4. *The elite coach understands that the coach and athlete enthusiasm-to-energy split is 10 total units. For instance, 5/5, 9/1, 2/8.*

5. CEO *to me: "You make three decisions a year that matter."*

1. The elite coach understands cost-to-benefit ratios.

In the mid-1980s, I walked into our first department meeting of the year. Our department head, who spent his life telling us the same thing over and over again, this time had a quick announcement.

"Dan, we need you to teach senior economics this year."

Three days before school started, I was given a class hated by student and faculty alike. I left the meeting and went to the library to check out some books because…

Like most of us, I knew nothing of economics.

Teaching this class continues to be the best coaching experience of my life.

I was often able to stay ahead of the class by two days. Quickly, I realized that teaching basic economics was the most enjoyable class I had ever taught. Every aspect of life leaped off the page, lecture and discussion. Everything was applicable to everything.

By God, I loved it.

The concept that leaped off the page most was cost-to-benefit ratios. It was the key to teaching, coaching and life.

I often make this tired joke about the key three "Fs" in life: Fitness, Finance and Relationships. The prudes just wrinkled their collective noses.

In the key areas of life, "little and often over the long haul" tends to beat out the instant. Yes, some people will take drugs and have better abs, but it's a not long-term solution. Some will take your cash in a get-rich-quick scheme and convince you to hand over your hard-earned money. And, maybe there is a way to seduce people with mental tricks, but that's not going to lead to celebrating a golden wedding anniversary.

Cost-to-benefit ratios are simple: There are strengths and weaknesses, pros and cons, good and bad with every decision you make. For every up, there is a down. Our job, as the big kids, is to understand this concept.

Yes, we can do more. But, do we get better?

Yes, we can add more load. But, do we get better?

Yes, we can take more fiber. But, do we get better?

Fill in anything you want. But, do we get better?

That is the cost-to-benefit ratio. Good coaches live in it.

It's hard to understand at first.

Yes, it, whatever *it* might be, might help. Yes, it makes sense. But, is it worth the time and effort...and the time and effort?

Sadly, usually, no!

2. The elite coach understands that enough is enough.

First, I want to explain something of historic importance: *Enough is Enough* is not the title of that famous Donna Summer song; that was *No More Tears*.

And, you are welcome.

> *Just look him in the eye and simply shout:*
> *Enough is enough*

I can't go on, I can't go on, no more, no
Enough is enough
I want him out, I want him out that door now
Enough is enough
Enough is enough
That's enough

There is a truth here. It's hard to learn. Conditioning athletes is easy: more running, more up-downs, more wind sprints. None of that helps…just so you know.

You can stretch until everyone is Gumby and moves like a green plastic man. Great. In most sports, you just nailed the coffin shut.

You can…

You get the point: You can do this and this and that and this until everyone is burned up, but only rarely will it help performance.

Enough is enough!

3. The elite coach knows to correct the correctable.

This is a concept, as mentioned earlier, that I learned from John T. Reed, who wrote about it in several of his books. Reed breaks down most things into areas of life you can improve (the correctable) and those things you *cannot* improve—he calls them "Zen."

He coaches baseball and lists the basics of baseball like this. In baseball, these are correctable skills (among many):

Catching a ball in the outfield

Sliding

Bunting

Waiting for a good pitch to hit

These would be Zen skills:

Hitting a baseball

Throwing a baseball accurately

Catching a grounder

Focusing on the correctable skills will improve a baseball team. It's like geometry. When you look in the mirror, you have certain "givens," as in a geometry proof:

Height

General features

Eye color (you can add lenses, but that's cheating)

Genetics and original geography (where you are from)

Home life as a child

Attitudes about the world in general

Like a geometry proof, one can take the givens and move on to prove things, or, rather, *im*prove certain things:

Physique

Hair decisions

Dress

Location

Career

Two biggest investments of life: You! And your spouse(s)

But, you can only correct the correctable. Sure, you can put lifts in your shoes, but, overall, you can't do much about your height. Still, you can make your wardrobe show your physique better, enhance your looks and make you look like a winner.

Keep this all within reason, of course. The haberdasher can do only so much.

4. The elite coach understands the coach and athlete enthusiasm-to-energy split.

This is something on which people don't universally agree. I go to workshops and hear the leader tell us that we (the coach, the head instructor, the leader) must come in with a ton of enthusiasm and energy and…pardon me, I was clapping and cheering so hard, I fell out of my chair.

I don't agree, and I have never have agreed with this idea, but, yes, there are times when I must pick the athletes up, dust them off and start all over again, as the song goes.

But, here is the thing: I'm not going to be in the ring, on the field or in the water with the athletes during performance. The athletes must learn to find the internal drive—the internal engines—of enthusiasm and energy, of calmness and concentration.

I call this "The 10 Units." The athlete and coach share a total of 10 units of enthusiasm or energy.

When I'm teaching the basics or am in a camp setting, I might be at an eight, and I will carry you along from your level of two. Together, we add up to 10 total units.

When you go home and email me about the long hours you spent on the field practicing, you gave nine, and I will give myself a one for replying to the email.

Sometimes, it's five and five. But, it depends on the situation. I want my athletes and clients to become big kids who own the path and goals.

The job of the elite coach is to make the big decisions. Yes, of course, build the foundation, work on weaknesses, fill in gaps, raise the standards and maintain the course, but our *real* job is making the big decisions…the tough calls.

5. CEO: "You make three decisions a year that matter."

I fly a lot. I end up in first class or business class most of the time. I've sat next to senators, a former presidential candidate (I didn't vote for him) and important business people. They like it that I know about fitness, and I like that they know about success. We sit, we drink and we share.

I was on a flight with a guy who sold his company for a billion dollars and was looking for the next adventure in his life. We talked for a long time about fitness and performance, and, if you have been paying attention while you've been reading, you know the basics of our talk.

He talked to me about the key to good leadership and coaching. He mentioned a friend of his who built a business into a billion-dollar enterprise and, basically, started a college. His key advice:

"You make three decisions a year that matter."

Decisions.

I am not sure there is a more complex word that everyone thinks is so simple. "*Cid*" or "*cis*" means "to cut or to kill." Homicide, suicide and scissors all share the same root: "to cut or to kill."

True decision making is rare.

Coming into the office and telling the manager to change coffee brands is just being a pain in the ass. Choosing fonts or picking the color of printed materials is simply not that big of a deal.

True leadership decides. It means you cut off or kill all the other options. And, it's rare.

"Folks, we are going to do THIS."

If a hand goes up for a question, the appropriate response is "Put that hand down."

Decisions—true decisions—are rare, and we don't do them very often.

When we decide something, we need to say goodbye to all the other options. For the record, those other options were not good or bad, naughty or nice. They were just other options, and we have decided to go another way.

When you make a big decision…make it. Be decisive.

And be done and gone and finished with discussing the decision any longer. Go do it.

My daughter, Kelly, now a mother and a teacher, reminds me about the secret to happiness. It comes down to how you answer this question:

"Do you see your work as a job, career or calling?"

I've worked with people who see coaching as a job. Often, a former high school athlete will slide through college and begin coaching and teaching. Usually, people who see this as a job will work to the letter of the contract. If practice starts at 3:00, they wander in while still checking messages on a smart phone. They take the check at the end of the week and go off to their "real" lives.

I am not belittling this choice. We have all taken on tasks to pay a bill or fill in a gap on a resume. Coaching as a job, in my view, would be the saddest way to spend every day. Oh, I have done it. I've said "yes" to things and wondered what I had gotten myself into many times in my life.

Coaching can also be a career. Certain college football jobs pay enough money to impact great-grandchildren and provide enough fame for 10 lives. Happiness there comes through trophies, rings and championships.

To some, coaching is a calling. It's something that transcends the day-to-day work in the gym or on the field of play. We can make an impact on the future. Yes, maybe some of our people will have trophies and rings and championships, but the lessons learned are more valuable than precious metals.

The elite coach understands all three. The best coaches raise us all up to a calling.

Shark habits and a pirate map for elite coaching

Coaching is an art and a science. True coaching balances the skill sets of a used-car salesman, a ship's captain and a cable TV comedy-show host. Knowing what you're doing is part of the battle. Implementing the right things is where the real art begins.

And, not to forget, even the most perfect plan and method has to be flexible enough to turn and change on the whims of life, the universe and everything else.

Let's look at some details.

1. *Constant assessment*

Certainly, there are formal tools for assessment, and they have great value. We can measure practically everything with standing long jumps, the Functional Movement Screen, heart-rate tests and all of the rest.

But, true coaching is *constant* assessment.

When something simply doesn't look right, you need to address it quickly and correctly, even if you don't have the precise problem sorted out. Sometimes it's hard to grasp. That's why a good coach never stops learning.

2. *Constant upgrading*

Whether it's books, articles, workshops or sitting in a bar, good coaches are always looking for a better way, a clearer path. Discernment is a rare skill, but the ability to pick and choose "better" among a host of options takes more time than any of us have in a typical lifetime. You need to trust others to carry some of the load of discernment for you.

3. *Ignore perfect*

Oh, I know your aunt is waiting to get in shape until the perfect diet and the perfect exercise plan is finally here. Every time I go to a party, people with a year's supply of calories in both hands will ask about the dangers of bacon, wine or coffee.

I strive for two things: pretty good and better. As long as we start off in this direction and gather ideas, equipment and materials that are better, I think we'll be okay.

4. *This isn't moral theology*

This marches hand and hand with "ignore perfect." Don't label equipment or exercises "good" or "bad." There is a time for everything under the sun, but maybe not today. An injury will change exercise selection, loading and repetitions, but it is what it is.

There is a time for planks and a time for explosive work. Carbs have great value, and sometimes we might want to eat fewer of them. But, it's not good or bad—it just is.

This, also, is a hard topic for young coaches to grasp.

5. *Everything works*

This is the toughest one. Every idea, every new thing and every old and moldy concept works. There is a part two to this:

Everything works…for about six weeks. When you fall in love with a new thing—the answer to all of your problems—circle the calendar on Monday of week seven.

That is the day you will discover, in perfect clarity, that everything works.

When you build a career, you will find lots and lots of six-week periods. Use each and every new idea, but remember number one: *constant assessment.*

Did it get you closer to or farther from the goal?

That leads us to the great next principle.

6. *Achieving a goal versus success*

This is the most important point I push on my athletes. You can get a goal and still be a failure in life. Be sure your genetics, geography, social and family life align to be the foundation of your focus. As you march toward a goal, ensure that you enjoy the travel, the friendships and the learning. These are as important as this "bell" you might want to ring down the road.

Certainly, attack and achieve your goals. But, enjoy the process and the fruits, too.

7. *After the peak is the cliff*

Mark Reifkind taught me this one. Goals and goal achievement are great, but…*now what?*

As you climb the ladder to success, take a moment to plan what you are going to do at the top! And, then, think about the route down.

8. *Self-discipline is a finite resource*

I use friends, family and everyone I can find to support me on the path toward my goals. The more communal you can make your goals, the less you have to stress and strain and choke your own free will.

It's much easier to show up and train with 10 people than to strive to push yourself out the door day after day.

9. *Fundamentals trump everything else*

The master is the one who masters the basics. Yes, it *is* that simple.

10. *Take a moment to appreciate those who went before you*

Thank your folks; thank your coaches. They won't be around forever.

Leave a legacy and make a difference.

Chapter **10**

The Secrets to Training

My life, as I have written before, changed after I walked over to the Orange Public Library in South San Francisco. I wanted to become a football player, so I picked up Eliot Asinof's book *Seven Days to Sunday* and read the book several times. Later, I found a copy of the book, bought it and memorized the story of the undersized linebacker, Kenny Avery. Everything he did, I did.

In the spring, he did the hurdles, shot and discus.

In the spring, I did the hurdles, shot and discus...and learned to turn in the discus. The book changed my life.

That first day at the library, the librarians had a book displayed in the recommended area. It was T. H. White's *The Sword in the Stone*. I loved the movie as a kid (I was probably the only person who actually loved it), and took that book home.

It took a while for me to get through it. That book made me a reader. I have read it at least once a year since 1971. During a quiet night in Cairo while overcoming massive dehydration from dealing with an internal parasite, I read *The Sword in the Stone.* It's not unusual to find me pulling my smaller copy out on a trip or on a quiet day to read it through again.

The title of my first book, the book that changed my family's life, is from the First Rule of the Foot from White's book: *Never Let Go.* What I never realized is that this book also taught me what I know about weightlifting and performance.

A quick note: In the book, a young King Arthur is referred to as "Wart," as it sounds like "Art" according to young Sir Kay. And, as I reflect my total geekosity of the material, the following version is from the edited *Once and Future King,* not the original *The Sword in the Stone* from 1938.

> *Wart felt his power grow.*
>
> *"Put your back into it," said a Luce (or pike) off one of the heraldic banners, "as you once did when I was going to snap you up. Remember that power springs from the nape of the neck."*
>
> *"What about those forearms," asked a Badger gravely, "that are held together by a chest?*
>
> *Come along, my dear embryo, and find your tool."*
>
> *A Merlin sitting at the top of the yew tree cried out, "Now then, Captain Wart, what is the first law of the foot? I thought I once heard something about never letting go?"*
>
> *"Don't work like a stalling woodpecker," urged a Tawny Owl affectionately. "Keep up a steady effort, my duck, and you will have it yet."*

A white-front said, "Now, Wart, if you were once able to fly the great North Sea, surely you can coordinate a few little wing muscles here and there? Fold your powers together, with the spirit of your mind, and it will come out like butter. Come along, Homo sapiens, for all we humble friends of yours are waiting here to cheer."

The Wart walked up to the great sword for the third time. He put out his right hand softly and drew it out as gently as from a scabbard.

- Power springs from the nape of the neck.
- Use those forearms held together by the chest.
- Find your tool.
- Never let go.
- Keep up a steady effort.
- Fold your powers together, with the spirit of your mind.

As I flip through the lifting journals I have kept since those days in 1971, I discover the same truths of pain, passion, failure and success bouncing off the pages.

1. Olympic lifting and kettlebell ballistics
2. Anaconda training
3. Killer app (see my book *Can You Go?*)
4. *Never Let Go* is my email signature line and the title of my first bestseller
5. Little and often over the long haul
6. Mental training in all its forms

Learn from Arthur, and pull the power of *The Sword in the Stone*.

Or, it might be even better to learn to hammer the sword into the stone!

Hammer and stone

Stu McGill is a genius…and a friend. His clarity in training athletes has changed my entire approach to performance. He pounds, and this might be funny in a moment, on twin concepts that make an athlete great:

+ Hammer
+ Stone

Because of throwing and American football, I have always used the concept of "bow and arrow" to teach my athletes the importance of loading the muscles, the pre-stretch or stretch reflex that leads to elite performance. It's right in the discus, shot put, javelin, and in tackling and blocking in American football.

I use the bow-and-arrow idea in all of my teaching. Just as the barbell passes the knees in the snatch or the clean, the chin and butt become the tips of the bow. The bowstrings are the hamstrings, and the explosion upward will be the arrow. I also use the concept to teach the important "C" position of the prestrike in all sports…including pitching and kicking.

As I think and rethink about the material, I realize the bow and arrow, a fantastic teaching tool for many things, seems to rub against one of my keys to proper training.

One of my foundational statements in training is "The body is one piece." This is a way to restate the concept of integrity, the moral and eschatological idea of, basically, always being the same person. The body is one piece is summed as integrity.

We are one piece, and I agree with the western tradition that we are as body, mind and soul "one piece." I often note that having diarrhea is going to make for a bad day to squat max. Breaking up (is hard to do) is going to have an impact on getting your Olympic lifts or hammer throws lined up correctly. Grief has a shocking impact on performance, and it's rarely like we see on television: Grief usually leads to bad, sad days.

Integrity is *you.*

What about everything else?

The *environment* is everything else. It can be an opponent, a shark, a wall or a football field.

When I talk about the "sixth movement" concept (anything you do in the weightroom that is not push, pull, hinge, squat or loaded carry), I often say that crawling and tumbling are "integrity with the *horizontal* environment" and climbing and swinging around in trees are "integrity with the *vertical* environment."

Stone work builds integrity, and hammer work is what we do to the environment. Now that I understand Stu McGill's idea better, I am getting clearer on what to look for in training methods to support stone-and-hammer work.

Stu has prodded me to really push this beyond my simple insight about bow and arrow. The hammer idea is using the hammer. BAM!!! To jump high, you hammer the earth as hard as you can, and then coach Isaac Newton takes over.

Action...REACTION!

Training the hammer is a lot like training the bow from the bow-and-arrow example:

- Basic skipping, bounding and sprinting

- Hill sprints and stadium steps

- Rack deadlifts

- The Olympic lifts

- Medicine-ball work (serious stuff, not what we usually see)

Hammer work is hinge work. Hammer work is leaping, jumping, bounding and sprinting. In the weightroom, we can help the hinge with:

- Mastery of the glute bridge or pelvic tilt...whatever you call it

- Loading the hip thrust

- Doing the whole deadlift family

- The kettlebell swing

Focus on the movements, not the muscles.

Learn the hinge while keeping the spine neutral—not straight or vertical; these are different things.

To be truly great, you need to get out on the field of play to hammer the ground. And, hammer your opponents.

But, and this is the great insight of Professor McGill, when you hammer the ground, your body can't sag and go floppity floopity. Your *column*, the area between your knees and neck (don't call it "core") must be *stone*.

If the energy wobbles off to your inner gelatinous goop, you lose the pop, the spring, the hop.

The pop
The spring
The hop

Those are the words that describe elite performance in most Olympic sports. In the equestrian events, we expect a well-trained horse to pop over barriers!

I was so close in understanding this. I know with Quadrant II people—collision sports and collision occupations—we do some exterior callusing, what I call "armor building." It has worked to get football players ready to play football and wrestlers to wrestle. See Appendix Five for a description of armor building, page 269.

Stone is like armor building, but not.

I was close with "anaconda strength," coaching the athlete into understanding the need for internal pressure. See Appendix Six for "anaconda strength" details, page 279.

Both armor building and anaconda strength are on the right track.

But, to take the hammer and put your chin on the rim of the basketball hoop, you need to be stone.

If you read those appendices, you will find deadlifts, lockouts, bear-bear and many other ideas for stone work. Here are a few more:

- Bear-hug carries
- Goblet squats with curls
- Goblet squats with heartbeats
- Double-kettlebell cleans
- Litvinovs (see Appendix Seven for Litvinov samples, page 285)

I'm still amazed by the pushback I get from some strength coaches against Litvinovs. Of course, I don't give my athletes drugs from a cookhouse kitchen either, so what do I know? Litvinovs have been a Godsend to many units of the U.S. military...and it's great for stone training.

We can establish a base of stone training in the weightroom. Stu has this list in his book *Back Mechanic:*

- The McGill curl-up
- The side bridge
- The bird dog
- And, let's add the kettlebell swing

The joy of a correctly executed kettlebell swing is that it's the hammer and stone...very fast. The kettlebell swing remains my go-to for both fat burning and building athletes.

Next, we need to take this to the field of play. The whole family of loaded carries naturally teaches "stone." Some sports demand a high level of stone just to get through a drill. Using sleds in American football is like blocking and tackling. Every minute of any martial-art activity is a lesson in stone training.

This is the true yin and yang of the strength coach and the technical or team coach: We walk together. Our job should be to build an appropriate athlete in body, mind, soul and spirit.

We hear the phrase: "We need to forge our athletes!"

"Nothing splendid was ever created in cold blood. Heat is required to forge anything. Every great accomplishment is the story of a flaming heart."
~ Arnold H. Glasow

I agree. And you need a hammer and stone to do that!

Training the aging athlete—training the active athlete

I sometimes get asked what I consider an "aging athlete." The answer is going to hurt some feelings.

If you are older than 22 and not making a living in your sport, you are an aging athlete. And, if you are older than 22 *and* making a living in your sport, you are *still* an aging athlete.

To be nice, I will call you an "active athlete."

But, each and every year, you are getting older. Sorry, but true.

In addition, I want you to have good quality of life as well as a big quantity of life. I can't repeat that enough.

Longevity is a crap shoot. Being in the wrong place at the wrong time isn't something we can fix with vitamins or a better morning regime. But, addressing the logical and basic stuff will put us in a position to deal with the bulk of life's minor challenges... and many of the major ones, too.

Let's apply proper training to the appropriate age bracket.

If you are an athlete, you should Olympic lift, deadlift, swing a kettlebell and do every loaded carry you can dream up. If you—or your athletes—need to be big for a sport, do the "sex drive" work, which we're going to talk about in a minute. If you are cashing million-dollar checks for weighing more than 400 pounds, we will deal with some issues down the line. But, until then, cash that check.

Cash that check. And remember: The checks you are writing with your body today will come due sooner than you think. You will need to cash *those* checks, too.

Training as we age

Let me repeat something again: I started lifting weights in 1965. I have more than half a century in the weightroom.

I think I am qualified to talk about junior high, high school, junior college, Division One and minor fitness celebrity strength training because I have lived, learned and languished at all these levels. I'm an expert on training with several full-time jobs, too.

Generally, I have trained too much, too long and too heavy. Many of my lessons from my career are this:

Do NOT do too much, too long and too heavy!

And, when I do find something that works, I seem to get away from it as fast as I can because…Sing it with me…*It worked so well, I stopped doing it!*

One thing my experience in the weightroom, field and classroom never prepared me for was turning 59. Or 49. Or 39…and you get the point.

If it's true that hindsight is 20/20, my vision of coaching for age is far better now than it was when I was a mere youth at, say, 55.

How do we train as we age? Do we go back out for high-school football so some guy with a towel around his neck can call us names and blow whistles? Do we pretend to join some elite military cadre and do a bunch of junk that leads to injury?

No.

NOOOOOOOOO!

We need to train age appropriately, and that is the most obvious thing I have ever said in my life. We need to train to build the qualities we need to ensure quality of life and quantity of life. Both are important.

Longevity is important.

So, yes: Don't die. And, don't die trying to work out so hard that you kill yourself!

As always, the devil is in the details. Let's talk about the specifics of training as we age.

A tip of the hat to Nick Rians from FitRanx for the age breakdowns we're using in this section. His company understands the need we have to compete and succeed in reasonable, logical steps based on age, size and gender. I follow his brilliant lead here.

Age group one: 16–35

Age group two: 36–55

Age group three: 56+

I base training on this principle: *The fundamental human movements done with appropriate reps, appropriate sets and appropriate load are the foundation of maintaining and improving human performance in all areas.*

The list I use for the fundamental human movements, as you've memorized long ago, is simple and to the point:

> *Push*
>
> *Pull*
>
> *Hinge*
>
> *Squat*
>
> *Loaded carries*
>
> *The sixth movement—everything else, but generally crawling, tumbling, climbing and anything that builds integrity with the environment*

When I talk with adults, I break the movements into three categories:

> *Sex drive*
>
> *Survive*
>
> *Thrive*

Sex drive means looking better and feeling better, and you can guess where this leads. In the weightroom, it's the hypertrophy moves—the push, the pull and the squat—that make us look better and drive that wonderful hormonal cascade that fills us with the Fountain of Youth.

Certainly, this is an important focus for turning back the clock in the aging process. These bodybuilding moves change lives for the elderly. But, and this is important, before you start worrying about looking great, feeling great and, um, improving your romantic life, you have to make it there!

So…sex-drive movements are the push, pull and squat. But, you have to survive to use those lovely muscles.

Survive comes in two parts. First, it's what I call "The Sixth Movement." This includes rolling, tumbling and break falling. If you slip, you will be happy that you know how to fall. If something really bad happens, the ability to climb a rope or just hang on for a while could be the difference between life and death.

I expect you to be able to do these for as many years into the future as you can:

- Stand on one foot for 10 seconds
- Hang from a bar for 30 seconds
- Standing long jump your body height (for distance, not height!)
- Squat down, hold for 30 seconds, and then stand up
- Farmer walk bodyweight for "some" distance (a few feet is nice; 100 yards is better)
- Get your butt to the ground, and get off it again by just putting one hand to the ground to assist (or none!)

Each of these will keep you out of the Old Folks' Home and give us a few extra seconds to help you if there's a flood, gas leak or rattlesnake scare.

Once we have "survive" and "sex drive" addressed, let's focus on thriving. *Thrive* movements are the hinge and loaded carries. Adding lots of swings and farmer walks will do wonders for our overall explosion and work-capacity needs.

Performance athletes need the thrive movements—the hammer and stone...the hinge and loaded carries. Everybody else could use those, too.

To review:

+ *Sex-drive movements lead to improvements in lean body mass, which leads to miracles in the hormonal cascade: push, pull, squat*

+ *Thrive movements, the hammer and stone or bow and arrow: hinge and loaded carries*

+ *Survival movements, groundwork, crawling and climbing (integration with the horizontal and vertical environments): everything else, or what we call "The Sixth Movement."*

Training appropriately for your age

Age group one: 16–35

The focus of this group should be the "thrive" movements. Anything that can make your bow and arrow shoot farther, your hammer pound more and your stone be stonier is what training is all about for this age group.

If you don't need size, you still need some "sex drive" work. You need to do a bit for the basic hypertrophy and mobility it provides.

And, survive.

Wait.

Survive?

Yep:

- ◆ Don't smoke.
- ◆ Wear your seatbelt.
- ◆ Learn to take a fall.
- ◆ TRY NOT TO BE STUPID!

One stupid thing would be to focus on the sex-drive movements, as many young athletes seem to do. These are fine, but too much and, as (once again) the cliché goes, you will look like Tarzan and play like Jane.

Remember: If you keep your weight under 300 pounds, wear a seatbelt and don't smoke, you can do a lot of dumb stuff and still make it to 55.

But, once you get there, now what?

This is also the age to take care of the basics of finances. Let's review this list from the pirate map section:

- ◆ *Remain debt free.*

- ◆ *Maintain an emergency fund with enough to cover minor problems (and keep it easily accessible).*

- ◆ *Save some money every month for some distant "Fortune Fund."*

- ◆ *Buy quality goods and services.*

- ◆ *Maintain your health with proper care and medical and dental check-ups.*

- ◆ *Choose wisely when it comes to matters of the heart.*

- ◆ *Invest deeply in your and your spouse's (!) education and career advancement.*

From ages 16 to 35, one can lay down the foundation of a successful and healthy long life.

+ To summarize, in age bracket one: *Thrive! Do the Olympic lifts. Do loaded carries.*
+ Maintain mobility and hypertrophy with appropriate sex-drive work, and look at surviving, both in body and bank, to some ripe old age in the future.

Age group two: 36–55

Age bracket two, those young devils 36–55, are quickly discovering something:

> *I walk past an ice cream store and get fatter!*
>
> *Does belt leather really shrink over time?*
>
> *Who is that old person in the mirror?*

Lean body mass is dripping off at this age, so athlete or regular Joe needs to train the sex-drive moves here. It's finally time to chase bodybuilding.

Finally!

Take care of finances. If you haven't started being a big kid about money, do another set of curls (joking...I don't know what to tell you if you haven't figured out money by age 36).

If you are competing, add those hammer-and-stone movements, and enjoy the rare air of competing past high school.

One simple way to manage training is to group workouts into "sex drive" days and "thrive" days. Michael Warren Brown and I came up with this idea for age-bracket two:

> *Three days a week of hypertrophy/bodybuilding (mixed with mobility and flexibility)*

Two days a week of hinges and loaded carries

Here's our basic circuit for three training sessions a week in the weightroom—there are videos of these on the *YouTube* channel "dj84123" if you need to see any of them:

> *TRX T pulls (try for about 15 reps)*
>
> *Double-kettlebell press (8–12 reps with lighter 'bells)*
>
> *TRX curl (pump those guns with around 15 reps)*
>
> *TRX hip rip (left knee down)*
>
> *Chins (change grips and reps on every round)*
>
> *TRX hip rip (right knee down)*
>
> *TRX double rows*
>
> *Double-kettlebell press (5–8 reps with medium or heavy 'bells)*
>
> *TRX Stoney stretch (both sides)*
>
> *Ab wheel*

We rotate through this three to five times. The idea is to finish feeling better than when we arrived, get a little pump and take care of global issues.

Two days a week of hinges and loaded carries:

Circuit

> *Farmer walk or bear-hug carry*
>
> *Scaled-down humane burpee*
>
> *15 Swings*
>
> *3 Goblet squats*

3 Pushups

15 Swings

2 Goblet squats

2 Pushups

15 Swings

1 Goblet squat

1 Pushup

Farmer walk or bear-hug carry (return to start position)

Repeat two to three times.

To summarize age bracket two:

♦ Focus on training the sex-drive movements, but don't be afraid to continue thriving.

♦ Keep an eye on survival!

Age group three: 56+

First…survive!

I would suggest exercise programs that get you down on and up off the ground, quality movement of any kind and opportunities to laugh, think and enjoy friendship.

As important as lean body mass was in age bracket two, this is the time it becomes an issue of life or death. Muscle is the Fountain of Youth!

Cultivate new relationships and keep learning. Try new sports and new activities. Find the sport you should have discovered in your youth.

Kindle new experiences and relationships.

Years ago, my brother Gary found himself "volunteered" as the middle school's throwing coach. He studied up on the throws (and asked his all-knowing brother) and soon began to enjoy throwing. He asked:

"Maybe I should pick up the throws as a sport?"

His wise brother responded, "In eight years, you will have as much or more experience than most throwers on the planet."

Today, he is a college coach, nationally and internationally ranked in the hammer throw, and spends his days throwing with Olympians and playing in the hammer ring. Physically and mentally, he is younger than when he started.

Chapter **11**

Standards...or How Will I Know When I Get There?

I'm ALWAYS BEING ASKED about standards. We can't just tell everyone to do the standards of elite jumpers and throwers, brush off our hands and walk away. It's a much more complicated issue.

If you're an aging athlete, use rankings to figure out how you're doing. In my sports, we get a new lease on life every five years. There is nothing more interesting than talking to someone a year away from the next group:

"I'm struggling now as the oldest in my group, but next year (eyes brighten, smile gets conspiratorial), I have a BIRTHDAY!"

The oldest becomes the youngest in masters sports, and it's fun to be part of it. But, we still hear a lot of this:

"How do I compare with others?"

FitRanx does a far better job than me on this. Nick Rians gives us eight levels of testing across both genders and the three age brackets covered previously in chapter seven.

Nick has taken the athletic-goal mindset, point A to point B, and applied it to the general population, what we're calling "everybody else."

For a general set of standards that is battle tested, let's try something simpler.

I am a big fan of the work of Paul Lysengos. Paul is a kettlebell enthusiast and a fantastic coach. He saw the same issues with his adult clients and put his mind to work.

This wonderful, simple set of standards looks and seems "right."

Paul Lysengos's men's standards

Squat Movement

1. Proper form in the goblet squat
2. Goblet squat: 24kg × 10
3. Double-kettlebell front squat: 32kg × 10
4. Bodyweight back squat

Press Movement

1. Pushups × 10
2. One-arm kettlebell press: 24kg × 5 per side
3. Double-kettlebell press: 32kg × 5
4. Bench press: bodyweight

Hip Hinge Movement

1. Hip hinge with proper form (standing, floor and loaded)
2. Kettlebell swing: 24kg × 20 (proper form)
3. Double-kettlebell clean: 32kg × 10
4. Barbell clean: bodyweight

Pull Movement

1. Batwings, thumbs in armpits, 16kg × 10 seconds
2. Bodyweight row on rings or a TRX × 20
3. Bodyweight row, feet elevated, × 10
4. Chinups × 5

Paul Lysengos's women's standards

Squat Movement

1. Proper form in the goblet squat
2. Goblet squat: 12kg × 10
3. Double-kettlebell front squat: 16kg × 10
4. Back squat: 135 × 5

Press Movement

1. Pushups × one (one excellent pushup)
2. One-arm kettlebell press: 10kg × 5 per side
3. Double-kettlebell press: 12kg × 5
4. Double-kettlebell press: 16kg × 5

Hip Hinge Movement

1. Hip hinge with proper form (standing, floor and loaded)
2. Kettlebell swing: 16kg × 20 (proper form)
3. Double-kettlebell clean: 16kg × 10
4. Barbell deadlift: 1.5 × bodyweight (or 135 × 5)

Pull Movement

1. Batwings, thumbs in armpits, 8kg × 10 seconds
2. Bodyweight row on rings or a TRX × 20
3. Bodyweight row, feet elevated, × 10
4. Chinup × one

If you can do a standard "here," but not "there," well, there you go! There's your gap!

Strive for the same number at every standard before you move up on your stronger movement.

More is fine. Just remember to add more in a reasonable manner that doesn't lead to surgery.

And, no, I don't listen to my own advice!

You get only one body in this life; use it and enjoy it. Feel better by moving better by moving more. Some of us call this concept "Train!"

Train.

Train appropriate to your age.

Train with appropriate reps, sets, loads and exercises.

Train with some fun.

Train with passion.

Train.

Assessing training

There is a gap in most strength coach's programs: How do we assess ourselves? How do we see if a program is working?

I have seen assessment tools come and go, ebb and flow, for a long time. I think there are two that will hold solid for me:

Standing long jump

Farmer walk with bodyweight for distance

The details are in *Can You Go?* but, basically, the issue is this: If after six to twelve weeks on a program the athlete's standing long jump and farmer walk got worse, the program might be a disaster. At best, it might just be bad.

Now, if the athlete gains a lot of lean body mass, the standing long jump may drop a bit or stay stagnant. That would be okay.

Almost universally, increases in the farmer walk are good to see, but decreases demand a discussion. If a training program decreases work capacity, grip strength and the ability to move under load, we need to talk about what is going on there.

The standing long jump and the farmer walk assess the job of the strength coach.

But, we expect more: We know have to use Kurt's "Five Whys" matrix. See page 73 if you've forgotten this one.

Let's say after a fine off-season, an athlete shows up with noticeably more lean body mass, a big bounce to the standing long jump and the work capacity of a semi-truck using the farmer bars. After the first performance, let's check.

Did you throw far or tackle, block and fall on the ball (or whatever the principle of performance in the sport)?

Yes? Good!

No? Why?

Generally, the athlete will loop back to the issues of arousal after early-season performance issues. Sometimes with a "new body," the athlete projects efforts for the early season that might also be a barrier to success.

"I'm so much bigger and more powerful that I will destroy all my personal records and be the greatest of all time!"

This can lead to anxiety and other issues—the bane of high performance. Arousal is the hardest issue to tame in the early season.

Great athletes often stumble out of the blocks, so to speak, early in a following season. Yes, they have more lean body mass, more power, work capacity and perhaps even better technique, but comparing the Nationals, the Super Bowl or the Olympic Finals to an early-season competition is almost apples and oranges—it's almost a different sport!

The scene: *a small college track meet six months after the Olympics.* After a solid finish but no medal at the Olympics, our hero strides to the event. Bigger. Stronger. Faster. More eager!

Official: "Anyone bring a measuring tape? I forgot mine."

Our hero showed up with an Olympic Final arousal level, but early season is early season. The events are delayed for all kinds of issues. The most common one is the total lack of planning by many of the officiating crews.

Today our hero will struggle with arousal levels. Our hero might not compete as planned.

So, next year, we will train our hero with a drill where he listens to officials forget things!

Assessing *off-season* training needs to be done through the prism of performance.

Assessing *in-season* training needs to be done through the prism of performance.

Assessing *everything* in athletics needs to be done through the prism of performance.

For the performance athlete, nothing matters save performance!

Experience: It doesn't have to be yours

Once we accept the fact that performance should be better than practice, practice time can be set up to support this truth. Training to tune in heart rate, arousal and tension preps the performer for elite results.

As a strength coach, I can support performance by focusing on what is truly key and important to success. It's not just "more"—it's focusing on what is important and crucial. Then, as appropriate, we try to match the training to the needs of performance.

The final step of the APE process is experience (see page 105 if you've forgotten the APE process, but for a quick refresher: Accept, Practice, Experience). The athlete has to learn not to wilt under the spotlight, but rather to embrace the stage and excel.

And, that was easy to type, and it was easy to read.

But the spotlight, the crowd and the noise can constrict performance like a boa.

There are two simple ways to get experience:

> *One: go out and gather some*
>
> *Two: hear the stories of others*

Both work!

I'm a firm believer that sharing experiences is one of the best ways to accelerate progress. We know that kids who come from wrestling or football families tend to be better at wrestling or football. It's obvious and true.

So, why aren't you doing it?

For almost 25 years, I sat in dorm rooms at Denison College at Discus Camp with Bill Witt, Mike Rosenberg, Greg Henger, John Murray and many other coaches, sharing the experiences of our past seasons. We talk about tricks and tips. We talk about how to beat superior athletes, how to overcome success (strange concept, but true: you can be too good too early) and how to mold a championship mindset.

The lessons seem to roll down the same rivers as every other field.

- Show up!
- Be early
- Little and often over the long haul
- Warmups don't matter; breakfast doesn't matter; nothing matters save performance
- One-percent improvement is still improvement
- Achieving a goal is not necessarily success

Bill tells wonderful stories about "getting the edge" on far-superior athletes. There is nothing illegal, immoral or unethical in his stories—he simply realizes that against a superior opponent, one might only have a thin opening to victory. So, Bill prepares his athletes to set a stage for success.

If a crack appears, Bill's athletes take advantage and win.

People love stories and stories about people

This was the advice given to me by the late Jack Schroeder, who took me under his wing as a writer when I wrote a weekly column for a regional paper. If I "connected" in an article I wrote for the newspaper, he'd come to my office and sit across from me. He would point at the article and say "here." I would look and he would tell me "this" was the line where people kept reading. This was the story or sentence that made people want to find out where I was going.

I knew when I didn't hear "here," an article wasn't going to get published.

People love stories about people's experiences.

Of course, from there, it's the job of the coach and athlete to build a checklist, monthly reminders, programs and plans to take other people's experiences and put them into daily practice.

Experience teaches appropriate arousal, tension and heart rate

The best-worst method

Years ago, I was sitting in a classroom at the Olympic Training Center, covering my answers on a test given to us by a sports psychologist. I noticed every other thrower in the room doing the same thing. The test was a tough one:

> *1. List the 10 best moments in your athletic career.*
>
> *2. List the 10 worst moments in your athletic career.*

It was an amazing experience. Many of us found that writing the "Best List" seemed to feed off of itself: This great day reminded me of that great day!

It was a wonderful feeling.

We all kept our hands covering the "Worst List."

"Look at your 'Best List.'"

"Look at number one...now slide over to your 'Worst List.'"

The doc didn't have to continue the point. Most of us found that our worst moments led directly to a best. It was illuminating for all of us.

Elite discus throwers, like football coaches, hate losing more than they like winning. Failure seemed to be the great engine of success.

Oddly, the moral of this story is "Embrace failure!"

You see, life isn't success *or* failure. People die. Bad things happen. Innocent people get hurt. Yes, "embrace failure" was right, but it was just the beginning.

The real lessons came next.

With a simple chart, I learned how to rig the game of life (and athletics) in my favor most of the time.

Before I show this in more depth and clarity, let's take a moment aside and remind everyone that this works well for athletes.

A few years ago, Lyle McDonald, one of the brightest minds in nutrition—his focus on *rigor* is legendary—asked me to do a psychological assessment. Lyle had worked, and continues to work, on the link between how we are mentally wired and how we relate to food generally and macronutrients specifically.

Whenever I take a test, there is always a "Well, yeah. Of course" moment when the data comes back. My wife and I took DNA tests and it turns out that I was blue eyed and hardwired to be a power athlete.

Well, yeah. Of course.

Lyle's work opened my eyes after this little endeavor. One part from his response email changed my thinking:

> *P is persistence and is related to some aspect of how the brain interprets negative reinforcement. Basically, people low in P tend to take negative reinforcement as a signal to stop doing something, which makes sense.*
>
> *People high in P (you) seem to have this reversed: They see failure or negative reinforcement as a challenge to*

overcome. Basically, you are likely to stick with any-thing you decide to do...almost regardless of if you're improving at it or not.

In fact, something that you're having trouble mastering is more likely to make you pursue it more.

~ Lyle McDonald

Track and field athletes are an odd lot. Most throwers I know played football, but hated the coach whistling and yelling at them. They carry a "chip on the shoulder."

Many jumpers are basketball players who want to just slam and not do all that silly stuff like defense and passing. Long-distance runners are legendary in their myopic introversion.

And, I love all of them.

American football coaches often note that they hate losing far more than they like winning. I understand that.

For you blessed normal people (and your normal clients), use these tools to mine the journey. You probably will find that some fasting, some walking and some lifting weights will lead to the bulk of the fitness and physique goals.

If you thrive on overcoming the odds, overcoming failure and overcoming obstacles, read on.

The assignment and the lessons

I leaned into the desk at the United States Olympic Center and started writing my "10 Best List" of my athletic career. I ended up with 22 items.

1. *Throwing 182' 3"*

2. *Snatching 314 pounds*

3. *Qualifying for the Nationals*

That's enough for this explanation.

1. I had thrown much farther than 182 in my career. In the discus, 180 feet with the two-kilo Olympic discus is the line in the sand when it comes to performance. Everyone recognizes this as a National-level throw and a solid performance. I had done this in college and in the years after college.

Yet, this time I had overcome a parasite acquired in the Middle East that took me out...almost from life, but completely from training or drinking alcohol for three years. I was married when I made this throw. I had two kids and two full-time jobs, teaching high school and English as a second language.

I lifted weights only twice a week in a spa with my friend John Price. We benched pressed, front squatted and did bodybuilding machines. Two to three days a week, I would get in some throwing.

This throw proved to me "it" could be done. "It" was living a life full of responsibilities and work and diapers and vacuuming... and I could still throw the discus far. I got a nice letter a few weeks after this, inviting me to the USOC for an Elite Discus Camp.

And at that camp, I wrote that list.

2. I started Olympic lifting in 1975. In my first meet, I snatched 187 pounds...just a little over bodyweight. Soon, it was 204, and then 209. Nine months later, it was 231. Over the next two years, with starts and stops, it edged up to 264, and then to a big 285 during my senior year at Utah State.

I lifted in lots of meets. I tried lots of programs. My snatch simply stalled. Sure, I was invited to meets where they had only 300 pounds of weight, total—lifted in a meet set up between the machines at the YMCA. I worried about losing a lift and hitting a fire engine.

It's not like it is now, where we do the Olympic lifts in big facilities with everything one could ask for at a competition.

Just saying.

Dave Turner called me up and asked if I could lift in the Utah Summer Games. I told him I was throwing there and that I would love to get a meet in that weekend. I had been training on something called "The One Lift a Day" program, which involves—let's all say this—*one lift a day.*

Monday
    Power snatch

Tuesday
    Front squat

Wednesday
    Cleans

Thursday
    Jerks

Friday
    Off

Saturday
    Light total in the O lifts

I was training about 10 to 25 minutes per workout as a warmup to drills throwing a handled ball into a wall. Each workout lasted well under an hour.

And, I was making the best progress of my life!

At the meet, I opened with enough to win and took 286 on my second for a lifetime personal record. Dave asked if I wanted to try something over 300. We didn't have any light record-breaking plates, so I jumped to 314 pounds.

And, I made it.

This was 17 years after my first meet. It was 13 years after my last personal record.

It remains at the top of my "What the Hell Just Happened?" athletic experiences.

3. *I was throwing well my junior year of college and flirting with both 180 feet and qualifying for the Nationals. And, I should have.*

At the University of Montana, between rounds, I looked over at our assistant coach, Ferron Sonderagger, and was trying to figure out what he was telling me.

He was telling me to duck.

I took a discus across the right side of my head. I could taste the metal. The next six months are a fog. If you gave me a choice, I made the wrong one. My handwriting morphed back to first-grade level. I had nightmares. I couldn't focus. I quit sports and almost quit school.

In October, I woke up. I started training and throwing again. Coach Maughan called my senior season at Utah State "the best season in the history of USU."

When I got in the discus ring for our home meet, I smiled, swung the discus back and qualified for the Nationals by well over five feet.

I guess I should explain one other thing: At the university level, radio and newspapers comment on each and every performance. Everyone knew I had "failed" the year before and didn't qualify.

I would like to defend myself and say that not a lot of people get back up after taking a discus to the head, much less to qualify for the Nationals.

My "Three Worst" list...as I wrote it that day

1. *Out of bounds at Sectionals*

2. *Third place as a sophomore*

3. *Regionals as a junior*

I find it interesting that three events from high school made my list. But, my coach told people I "was a choke," an athlete who couldn't handle pressure.

I'm not sure labeling a 16-year-old as a failure is good coaching.

Overcoming this label inspired me through my junior-college years and drives me to be better at coaching athletes today.

1. Out of bounds at Sectionals

My high school coach had an odd way of inspiring fine efforts—everything out of his mouth was cynical, sarcastic or negative.

"At best," he said to me early in my senior year, "you will get over 150 feet." That season, I threw 170 feet at a bodyweight of 162 pounds. He would tell me things that just weren't right, like spinning on your heels in the discus throw was the proper way to throw.

That's just not right!

In addition, there were massive issues at home. My father, of Blessed Memory, was going through a period of heavy drinking. He got his second DUI somewhere around this time and had lost his license. There was no money for me to go to college, so I thought that throwing the discus far would open the doors for me.

It would.

Just not yet.

As the season wound down, I was improving almost daily, and I was winning a lot. Then, the teachers at my school went on strike. My brother Richard was on the staff, so my family was with him. The school closed for two weeks, with limited classroom access.

Pete Giachetti, another coach, told me I had to go to school on competition days to be eligible. It was a joke: I signed up for six periods of swimming and went home.

I won the League, took second at the Regionals (with the stomach flu), and headed off, with Mom and Dad, to the Sectionals.

I needed a good throw. My first throw fluttered, but my next throw put me right in the thick of things. I needed a good third throw to move on. The wind picked up, and I adjusted a bit to the right.

I nailed the best throw of my life.

Except it went just barely out of bounds. My little adjustment was too much.

My coach walked over—he had rarely spoken to me since early in the season—and said, "I will never understand why you moved your starting position."

Me neither, actually. I will never understand that.

But, I didn't go to State, and it was a long ride home. I had shoved everything into that one bucket: Go to State.

And I failed.

2. Taking third place as a sophomore

The North Peninsula League (NPL) was a storied football and track-and-field conference back in the day. The National Football

League has enjoyed many of our alumni, and my high school track team would still dominate.

This story is quick: I had a great early season and was pressing too hard to improve. At the NPL Finals (the league championship), we competed at Serramonte High School in a fog-filled windstorm that ruined the flights of my cheap rubber discus. I lost to much larger athletes who just hucked and chucked the discus.

The top two moved on to Regionals. I took third. One of the two was my teammate, and I offered to train with him. He showed up only once that week, and my coach told me to get ready for football.

3. Regionals as a junior

On March 30th of my junior year, I hurt my knee badly. I needed stitches and was on crutches for two weeks. I had tripped on a rock and ripped an ugly hole in my knee.

Those two weeks were important. Not competing and holding a clipboard got me going again. The first meet back, I broke my personal record and improved each and every meet after that.

At the NPL Varsity Finals, I was the smallest by far, but I won with a nice throw of 144' 10". I weighed just over 150, so this was good, but I knew I had more.

At the Regionals, I got there early and threw a little. Every throw was over 150. So, I kept throwing...and left all my stuff in the warm-up area!

I didn't place. Looking back, I was just stupid.

The autobiographical list

After the "list session," one of the docs asked me to dig deeper into this because I was older than the other participants. He asked me to do my autobiography, my "real life" Best-Worst List.

Oddly, I had sports highlights in my autobiographical Best-Worst lists, but the order was different. Three decades ago, I wrote this story of the top item of my "Best" list:

In my closet, there is a small trophy that bears a stamp "S.V. 67." For the record, it stands for St. Veronica's, 1967, the first trophy I ever received. I got it one year before my wife was born.

Although I often joke about my funeral, for example, having Frank Sinatra's One for My Baby, One More for the Road *as a closing song, I am serious when I ask that somebody remember this trophy. It's a lesson in, well, how God, Life and the Universe work.*

I was the world's worst baseball player. My batting average was three zeroes. I hated sports, while my brothers were getting their pictures in the local sports section on a weekly basis. As the right fielder, I was safe...until I batted. Then I would close my eyes, swing like mad three times and sit down.

And, of course, we were heading for the championship game. I went to the local high school the night before the game and decided to learn to hit. Throw the ball up, close my eyes and swing. Ball up, close eyes and swing.

As I tried to learn to hit, one of the local high school heroes, Dale Kursten, saw me trying and failing, and walked over and gave me a few lessons. "Keep your eye on the ball, swing level and make contact." A few easy hits later, he said goodbye.

And, like all great stories, everything came down to the last inning. With two outs and a man on third, our captain turned and asked, "Who's up?"

Me!

"Oh, great. We are going to lose."

Well, with that pep talk, I walked to the plate. Dale's words echoed: "Eye on the ball, swing level, make contact."

And, I did. The ball slid between the fielders, and I made it to first base. The guy on third scored, and we tied up the game.

Later, we would win.

A few weeks later, I was given that trophy.

At my sister's 20-year high school reunion, she mentioned this story to Dale. It didn't register. Oh, he had heard about my athletic career, but was stunned to discover he had anything to do with it.

Yet, I point to those few minutes of his guidance as a turning point.

Those few minutes with Dale shaped my life.

On the other side of the paper is a list of "worsts," and they are rough to think about. Usually, what starts off with joy on the "worsts" lists ends up in pain.

As I reread the story about Dale, I think I know why I became a coach.

My worsts list

1. *The first month after divorce*
2. *Lindsay's emergency birth*
3. *Portland State phone calls with soon-to-be ex-wife*

Assessing the best and worst lists

It seems logical and obvious, but my favorite moments seem to be when I overcome things, surprise myself or serve in the underdog role.

My worst moments in the area of performance are when I don't live up to a standard I have set for myself.

Okay, great. How do I use this information?

It was the next assignment that changed my life and my athletic career.

The bubbles exercise

This is easier than you may think, but the results will leap off the page. The assignment given to me by the sport psych docs was this:

1. *Put a successful performance in the middle of a blank piece of paper.*
2. *Draw a circle around it.*
3. *Then, in free form, write any thoughts that come to mind. Anything you remember is helpful: friends, family, food, sun tan or sunburn, food, noises, traffic, hotels, whatever.*
4. *Circle these memories. Then, using arrows, connect them as you see they connect. This is important; there might not be a logical explanation (yet!) why you connect this memory to that memory until you work through the whole exercise.*

> 5. *Step back and look at the whole picture. At first glance,*
>   *what leaps out at you?*

When I looked at that sketch in 1991, I simply said, "People."

When I do well, I am in community. I am a communal creature.

When I do well, I can list the stories and conversations.

At this track meet, Paul noticed that the home throwers, San Jose State, were starting just to the left of me in the ring. I had learned my lesson back in high school not to shift my feet...but, I trusted Paul. I moved over a few inches, found the concrete was much better there, and threw my lifetime best.

That was to be the last time my mom would ever see me throw—she died soon after.

Friends are listed on my sketch...and family. My professors, to a person, all took me aside that week and wished me good luck.

When my life goes sour, I seem to be alone. This is much clearer in the autobiography best-worst list where my divorce, my daughter and wife both nearly dying, and the period just before my divorce when I was studying Turkish at Portland State University collectively take the top three spots.

In each case, I was alone. I moved into a basement apartment with a sleeper sofa; the doctor shouted, "We are going to lose them both!" and I slept in a dorm with cockroaches, taking miserable phone calls from my soon-to-be ex-wife.

Now what?

Knowing this about myself, I now arm myself with community. At the Pleasanton Highland Games, I walked into the Games not knowing a single person. Someone in the crowd asked, "What's under your kilt?" and I answered with the usual offensive retort.

We laughed, I introduced myself, and he brought his family over to cheer me on.

Soon, it was a group. Finally, on my winning caber toss, the whole crowd was chanting, "Danny, Danny, Danny."

These days, every morning at 9:30, I open my door and train with anybody in the world who shows up to train with me. I need community to train, to compete and to perform.

I make communities intentional.

I call them "intentional communities."

When I compete, travel, work or go to dinner, I strive to invent these communities. I strive to turn every occasion into an opportunity for community.

1. *After workouts, I eat at the Landmark Café.*
2. *Wednesday nights, I join a group at Brio.*
3. *Several times a year, I invite everyone I know to Practice Thanksgiving.*
4. *I went to Discus Camp over the same weekend every year for 25 years.*

Whatever I do, I strive to build community because it makes *me* work better. I know the manager, I know the wait staff, I know the cafeteria ladies. I say "Hello," "Thank you," and "How are you today?"

It's nothing fancy, but it helps me achieve and succeed.

The bests and worsts lists and bubbles exercise revealed how I can bear the fruits of my experiences. The investment was a few pieces of paper and some emotional time.

If you do this, the results can change the way you perform in every area of your life. Using your experiences is wonderful and insightful. You also need to harvest (steal!) other people's experiences.

The horizontal community

I consider the horizontal community to be friends, family, team and community. These are people alive and well, of whom you can ask questions and get some feedback. I talked about this in *Can You Go?* and I include that section in Appendix Two on page 229.

I talk with my competition in places like Facebook and via email before we meet on the field. It's not to toss rocks and stones at each other; it's to ask about the little things. I know some things about throwing in Spokane that will help you throw the discus better, but I also might need to know what's going on in Austin or Orlando.

Sacramento State, the site of many major track meets in the USA, is nearly impossible to find the first time you go there. Sacramento was laid out either by madmen, lunatics or comedians, and you simply can't get there from here.

It's like the old Irish joke, "Which way to Dublin?"

"Well, I wouldn't start from here!"

If you are going to compete at Sac State, get there a day early and drive around a bit. Or hire out your trips, as I learned the second time I went.

This little nugget might make the difference between winning, placing or losing. Meet directors often live in the area of the competitions, so they are *terrible* at giving advice about hotels: They literally never stay in them. Someone else's experiences may save you some really bad nights of (non)sleep. I don't know why meet directors love hotels that are overpriced, horribly located and harbor outlines of homicides on the floors in the rooms. But they do.

In every area of life, there are people who have walked through the door before you, been to that city and done what you are doing. Ask them questions.

Talk to those who have walked the walk.

The vertical community

I've been lucky to have natural storytellers as coaches. Dick Notmeyer had a story for every problem in life. He always knew someone who had been in the same situation and overcame it with…

Front squats

Protein drinks

I am joking only a little! Everyone who worked with Dick can tell you the same thing, and I love him for it.

"Dick, I just got divorced."

"Dan, sorry."

Insert story. Moral: Front squats and protein drinks.

"Dick, I failed at the Nationals."

"Dan, sorry."

Insert story. Moral: Front squats and protein drinks.

"Dick, I'm getting too old to compete."

"Dan, sorry."

Insert story. Moral: Front squats and protein drinks.

And, I loved every story.

Coach Maughan had a great story about Glenn Passey forgetting how to throw the discus at the Nationals. Glenn was so nervous, he just forgot!

Of course, the moral of the story is that the Nationals are so pressure filled that even a future four-tour Vietnam helicopter pilot got nervous.

A vertical community is passed down. You'll recognize it when you hear these terms:

1. *We used to have a kid like you…*
2. *One time…*
3. *It's going to feel like…*

4. *Well, we expected this...*
5. *Remember how...*
6. *We used to do this thing...*

Storytelling is an art form that can sometimes be missing from a coach's quiver. It's worth the time as a coach to learn more about storytelling.

Good storytelling involves:

1. *A character*
2. *A problem to be solved*
3. *A twist in the story*
4. *An answer to the problem!*

I tell a 12-year-old girl or boy the story of how Eric Lindquist was so nervous at the state meet, he could remember only the first thing I ever taught him. He did that and added 33 feet to his all-time best discus throw, and became state champ by crushing everyone on that first toss.

That will be you in a few years!

"So, what did Eric do?"

Ah, the hook is set; let me reel it in. He picked up his right foot first at the back of the ring and let the feet do the work. As Coach Maughan told me, "Danny, if your brains were in your feet, you would throw farther."

His feet won him a state title.

The former athlete is the character, the problem is the goal, and the twist is the fun part. Every athlete finds a way to make a great story. I then take those lessons and fill the next batch of athletes with the answers to these twists.

Sadly, when you have a huge, athletic, fast and lean kid who dominates the opponents, the stories don't seem as fun. As we saw with the bests and worsts lists, the best stories involve overcoming great odds.

We also practice the various scenarios of the past. We embellish the stories, add additional twists and attack the appropriate arousal, tension and heart-rate levels.

I find it helpful to make lists of areas that cost games, championships or victories. For American football, these five things are crucial to winning close games:

1. *Catch the punt*
2. *Retrieve onside kicks (either kicking or receiving)*
3. *Two-point conversions (scoring or defending)*
4. *Defending a last-minute trick or gadget play*
5. *Staying in or going out of bounds to burn or save time on the clock*

Don't wait until the last second to talk about saving the last second!

I sit in the front row at workshops so I can focus on the speaker. Workshops are great places to pick up the stories and experiences of others to add them to your toolbox.

Make lists of things that are crucial to success and to avoiding failure.

Books, magazines and movies can be helpful, too. Sports movies have become filled with clichés, but there are still a few that can layer an experience portfolio. I find sitting in a room with other coaches as valuable as graduate school when it comes to getting the edge as a coach.

Get the stories.

Tell the stories.

Then, in practice, find ways to mimic those situations that lead to winning or losing. Add some new twists, some additional problems, and let the athletes find the path to success.

With experience, it doesn't have to be yours to be valuable.

To review APE

Accept...

>   ...that performance should trump practice.

Practice...

>   ...the keys to your sport.

Ensure proper arousal, tension and heart rate throughout the program.

Build the hammer and stone.

Experience...

>   ...fill yourself with other people's insights and experiences.

Know that roadblocks are coming, and embrace them when you get there.

Experience is a great teacher, *but it only teaches the teachable.*

Chapter 12

A Quick Summary of *Now What?*

WARREN BUFFETT'S NAME GETS tossed around all the time. If you get the nod from Warren that your company is good, enough people will invest to ensure you have the money to make this company "pretty good."

He was once asked by Charlie Rose how we often go from very good ideas to very bad ideas. Buffett answered:

> *"First come the innovators, who see opportunities that others don't and champion new ideas that create genuine value. Then come the imitators, who copy what the innovators have done. Sometimes they improve on the original idea; often they tarnish it. Last come the idiots, whose avarice undermines the very innovations they are trying to exploit."*

I can't summarize the fitness field any better. Innovators like George Hackenschmidt, Thomas DeLorme and Percy Cerutty, as well as the great research from Vlad Janda, give us all the answers:

+ Strengthen what is weakening.
+ Stretch what is tightening.
+ Increase load appropriately.
+ Keep it reasonable.
+ If you want greatness, you really have to pour in the time, intensity and passion.

You might recognize this as a pirate map. I would also argue that if you followed this list, you would be on your way to practicing appropriately.

The imitators quickly saw that you can't make money giving sound advice. Trust me, one barbell set will answer the bulk of your equipment needs forever. Certainly, kettlebells and suspension trainers and ab wheels will do a lot, but if you bought a standard 310-pound barbell set in 1954, you still have the basics covered.

And that became the issue: How can we make money off you if you don't buy *something* all the time? The imitators began to quickly push magic machines with scientific levers and ratios that promised bigger, faster and stronger.

They failed, of course.

Today, we tend to see the idiots. "Insanity" is a workout system now. We have muscle confusion, people terrorizing their abs and others trying to convince us that some ancient potion is the answer to all questions.

It's perfectly okay to train the good, old-fashioned way with some science and experience backing you up.

In the weightroom, do the fundamental human movements:

Push

Pull

Hinge

Squat

Loaded carry

Keep the reps and sets between 15 and 30 total reps. Like three sets of eight or five sets of five, the classic programs intuitively lived in the numbers the researchers discovered in the lab.

Increase load appropriately.

If you need to incinerate fat, you might want to consider long walks before you consider bone-breaking and joint-jarring protocols. And after you walk, take some time to stretch those muscles and roll through the joints with some mobility work.

The innovators knew this.

The imitators tried to trick us into something else.

And the idiots? Just log onto the internet.

We can do better.

Master the fundamentals; stick to the basics. Take a long walk. It works.

That is principle-based training, and the experience of others holds it as true. If we need to perform, we apply appropriate practice because we want our performance to trump our practice.

And, you know that.

You have always known that. Now, apply this truth.

As I told you in the beginning, don't ignore the obvious.

Appendices

Shark Habits and a Pirate Map for Time Management

1. FILL UP YOUR CAR'S GAS TANK whenever it drops to half-full. When you have half a tank of gas, there is always a gas station. There is no line at the gas station, and, moreover, you are just cruising around doing a few things. But when the "gas empty" warning light comes on, you will be in a desert with a woman giving birth. Be proactive and always fill up before you need to fill up.

2. I visit the local lube and oil shop every three months. I always have someone go with me, and then we go to lunch. I drop off the car, listen to all those annoying things that need to be replaced (always replace wipers and filters when prompted), we go eat lunch and the car is always waiting when we're finished. It keeps the car running longer and safer, and I never notice the time strain.

3. One last car issue: Replace your tires and battery long before you need to replace them. Perhaps it's because I drive on snowy roads and deal with cold mornings, but NOTHING kills a day or two or three like a flat tire or a dead battery.

4. Start compiling a house list. For your furnace filter, write down the measurements. I have two, so when I buy filters (I buy them in bulk), I have my little card that says "20 × 20 × 5" and "16 × 20 × 1." No other size will fit, by the way. Anytime you use an item, check to see if you have a replacement.

5. Have a master house or apartment list. If you have weekly chores, write down the day you do them. Tuesday night is garbage night, as the garbage man comes on Wednesday. You only forget that once. If you have annual items, write them down. In April and May, you might have chores to prep the cooling system—write them down. In October, you may have winterizing chores…write them down. Clearing this list clears your brain.

6. And while we're on lists, make a shopping list that relates to you and your needs. There are going to obvious ones most of us will buy: eggs, butter, veggies, fruit, but I would also include items you should always check off when you go to the store. Toilet paper, paper towels, Ziploc bags and garbage bags are easy to forget and really, really hard to substitute for one another. Most experts in time management usually say to shop once a week, and don't go back to the store that week. Josh Hillis argues that the hardest workout of the week should be shopping for food and food preparation. According to him, the harder you prep your food, the leaner your waistline.

7. This leads to a key time-management tool: Learn to "touch" everything just once. When you open your mail, have three options.

My first option is always the garbage can. Next, if a response is needed, respond immediately. If you don't have time to deal with it, don't open the mail yet! When you open the mail, have paper, envelopes, checkbook and stamps nearby to deal with anything that comes up. Finally, if it's something to read or look at later, keep a large manila envelope to store the magazines or letters or catalogs. Empty that on the first of every month.

8. The same applies to email. Email was once considered the cure to inefficiency in the workplace. This was before kitty videos, fantasy football and sexting. The same efficiency rules apply to email: Delete it, respond to it, or file it. Try to respond in five or fewer sentences, too.

9. Where is your workout gear? I live an interesting life where I can basically roll out and train anytime I want. If that's not your situation, I suggest that most people keep two packed training bags. If you commute or drive your car a lot, always keep one in there, packed and ready to go. If you go from work to home before you go to the gym, there's a really good chance you won't go to the gym.

10. Finally, it's okay to rethink the way you train if life is getting cluttered. I applaud the weekend-warrior mentality, where you train hard and heavy on both Saturday and Sunday. Kick in a moderate or even an easy workout on Wednesday, and you have a pretty good training template. Use some of the weekend for shopping, food prep and training, and it will leave your weekdays more open for the realities of life.

The Horizontal or Intentional Community

I'M SURE ALL OF US HAVE THIS issue some days: Today I had no interest in training. My gym, which serves the dual purpose of being a two-car garage, was nine degrees. Alice Lopez always gives us the temperature in Celsius, and when she says it's "minus whatever," it doesn't make me excited to train.

The night before had been a long night of travel and a cough that found itself only just as I nodded off. No, I didn't want to get up.

I didn't want to train.

But, it didn't matter. Why?

One of my greatest training tricks and tips is this: *I have an intentional community.* Sure, all of us know about training partners, and the great ones in history, like Arnold and Franco, have always nodded to their training partners as a "secret to success."

Intentional communities are a bit bigger and deeper than training partners. First, these involve a lot more people. Each of us brings something and, honestly, the most important gift is showing up. Second, an intentional community always welcomes more people to join in the fun.

Frankly, it's the new people who provide much of the direction. Most of us in our current group have been training for more than a decade. Now, that's great—congratulations and cigars to all of us.

The downside of training so long is that we can easily forget the path. When a new person joins our group, we ask simply: *What do you want to work on?*

The answer can transform the next few weeks of training. Many people really want to learn and master the squat, but years of office work or poor training has made the basic movement either unwatchable or even dangerous.

So we all step in with our gifts. Samantha Halpern is a physical therapist and might note that the person needs some of this corrective or that stretch. Marc, her nutritionist husband, might add several points about the basics of good habits that extend well beyond the day's workout. Mike Brown might then take the person aside and find the right regression for the squat that clears things up, from rocking on the floor to holding on to the pole and squatting. That's just a typical day.

All of this can be done between sets of lifting and general training. Very often, most of us will be doing the correctives and regressions the new person is doing because, well, it's really a good idea.

Intentional-community training also has another boon: I have a lot of experience in the weightroom, but sometimes I am grouchy and tired. What I need is the youth and energy from my group to get my engine started. I like to offer them in return some positive feedback, some corrections and a general sense of "This all is okay."

Originally, my first group started when I moved back to California a few years ago. Dan Martin, now a retired East Bay firefighter, asked if we could get together sometime to train. While the movers were still unpacking boxes, I drove down to Coyote Point, and Dan and I started a training group. Between piles of goose poop, we stretched, strained and trained. We met only once a week, but all of us looked forward to that session.

When I returned to Utah, a group of young guys from the university asked if they could train with me twice a week. Soon, it was three. Now, it's five.

Once, when I visited my doctor, he asked me if I trained. I said, "At least an hour a day." His response, "I have to admire your discipline." I was honest with him: I get out of bed only because there will be people showing up at my door, ready to train.

Intentional communities also offer an additional advantage to those of us living (and often suffering) through the Information Age: We get a chance to hear summaries of blogs, books, articles and movies throughout the training session.

A typical day:

"Did you read that article on training adductors on website X? What a waste." Mental note: don't read it.

"This new book on habits and training is well worth a read." Borrow it.

"I can't believe how good this movie X is...I was stunned." Might be worth a view.

Since we are all internet savvy and interested in the best and brightest tools for fitness, health, longevity and performance, we share ideas across the whole swath of media, and then we get back to the squat rack.

I have been lifting since 1965 (yes, you read that right). That's a lot of six-week programs and crazy ideas and bad decisions. Of all the things I have done, *nothing* compares to the quality of having an intentional community.

Are there problems? Sure. A common one is this: We have some people training for a kettlebell cert while the guys over here are doing *Mass Made Simple*. I might be doing a 21-day challenge of this kind or that. We have to ensure the equipment gets used in some kind of order.

The upside is that most of us have squirreled away a few extra straps, bands, 'bells or wheels, so we fix a problem like this by tossing more stuff in the pot.

Dan Martin calls this concept "Virtual Stone Soup." I realize now that most people don't know this fine story, so here is a bland example:

> *Some travelers come to a village carrying nothing more than an empty pot. Upon their arrival, the villagers are unwilling to share any of their food with the hungry travelers. The travelers fill the pot with water, drop a large stone in it, and place it over a fire in the village square.*
>
> *One of the villagers becomes curious and asks what they are doing. The travelers answer that they are making "stone soup," which tastes wonderful, although it still needs a little bit of garnish to improve the flavor, which they are missing. The villager does not mind parting with just a little bit of carrot to help them out, so it gets added to the soup.*
>
> *Another villager walks by, inquiring about the pot, and the travelers again mention their stone soup, which has*

not reached its full potential yet. The villager hands them a little bit of seasoning to help them out.

More and more villagers walk by, each adding another ingredient. Finally, a delicious and nourishing pot of soup is enjoyed by all.

Our communal training sessions are of this variety. We all bring tools from equipment to life experiences to sandwiches. We gather and train, work on issues and improve a little. We again fall in love with movement and muscle. We reignite our passion for "all of this."

I have been training in groups for so long that sometimes I ignore basic principles I learned the hard way years ago. One of the keys to working in a group, especially in something physical, is to understand that you—and perhaps this is even literally true— become part of an organism. A group becomes a living being.

You may have found yourself running "gassers" in a sport and realized there is no way you would ever put yourself through this crap. That's why group training has such a big impact on long-term success: You do things you might not do otherwise, even with the best intentions.

We humans have this odd ability to handle more suffering if we do it in a group. Moreover, it also seems more fun. I have had people vomit on my shoes and say, "Thank you" for the opportunity to do the work.

For the record, today was one of the best workouts of my life.

Appendix 3

Goal Setting

I'm always thinking about goals, goal setting and how I as a strength coach can make a difference.

I've been in my coaching career a long time. I started coaching around 1979, though my neighbors always say I was coaching them when we were kids, so I guess my career probably started a decade before. I used to teach all the kids in the neighborhood how to play football so we could have extra kids to play.

As I look back, one of the areas that was always the most difficult for me with athletes was goal setting. You see, I had such clarity as a kid about what I wanted to do.

I wanted to play in the National Football League. I wanted to play probably as a linebacker, but I was fine with playing college football for anybody. None of that ever happened, of course, but that's where the story begins.

Early on, I read the book *Seven Days to Sunday* by Eliot Asinof. On Wednesday, he introduces one of the players by the name of

Ken Avery, who was a linebacker. I thought his story was *my* story. He threw the discus. He shot put. He ran 800 meters and did the hurdles. In track season, that's what I did.

Ken did all kinds of things, and I misunderstood a lot of it. He did ballet and gymnastics, as well as tons and tons of pushups and sprints. I later found out he also lifted a lot of weights. I didn't know this at the time, but figured it out myself.

I got into the discus and the shot, the 880 and high hurdles. I was a pretty good hurdler, but I wasn't good enough to be an 880 runner along with my other interests. The shot I was never very good at because I didn't really try. Of course, in the discus at my first meet, I took probably 19th or 20th out of 19 or 20 people. Then, I built myself up to my second track meet, where I won by two inches. Afterward, the discus became my goal.

Right after this event, my brother Richard took me down to Track and Field News, where we bought a copy of the *Track and Field Omnibook*. The book covered Ralph Maughan at Utah State University, and that's when I decided to go to Utah State. I was a 118-pound high school freshman who threw the discus 103 feet, and I set my sights on being a Division I discus thrower.

To me, this is how goal setting works.

You'll notice there's a story behind my goals, and that's really an important part of the goal-setting process. When I talk with a guy who says he wants to do x, y or z, for me the story is important—the history, the background. I'm dealing with a person who showed up with a goal, and it helps to see where it's coming from.

When I was growing up, I remember a lot of guys in Pennsylvania, the sons of coal miners, who would use football as their way to not work in the coal mines. These guys were rough and tough. They knew this was their chance. When you know this type of story, it helps us understand the athlete.

People talk to me about goal setting all the time. The problem is there's a huge disconnect between what I hear and what you're saying.

It came to me not long ago that in the process of goal setting, there are two things. I call them—very fancy—Point A and Point B. Point A is where you are, and Point B is your goal.

With my elite athletes, they always know where they want to go—Olympic trials, Division I athlete, NFL, play three more years in the NFL...or they want to keep their career going longer. That's all laudable and are all wonderful things.

What I realized is that I work with people from a group that represents not even one percent of the population. The sheerest, thinnest wedge of the population I work with are people who know what they want. The problem with my athletes isn't their goals. They always know where they want to go. They just don't know where they are, which is why you'll notice I talk about assessments in so much of my writing.

I constantly assess my athletes. We do Functional Movement Screens. We have a back squat for repetitions. We have bench press for repetitions. We have max bench press. We have max back squat. We do a standing long jump and some carries. We have the assessments from *Can You Go?*.

I compare your pullups to your bodyweight bench press numbers. I have this little soda-bottle-cap test I do with my athletes. I have an overhead squat test. It takes up reams of paper, to be honest with you, especially when I have a chance to really work hands on with a person.

Here's what we do with all this information. You have somebody who wants to be a Division I discus thrower. Just by getting the thrower to do something he's never done, which is usually loaded carries and sometimes the deep squat, and just by getting him to realize he needs to squat or do sleds, hill runs or whatever, by showing him where he is in Point A, we highlight much faster where he needs to go to get to Point B.

This is the role of the assessment—figuring out where you are and then taking an honest look at Point B, your goal.

"I'm here now."

The problem with most elites is that they know what they want. They just don't know where they are—that leap is just a little clouded. This chasm they have to leap across is foggy. They know there's another side over there. They just don't know how far they have to jump.

Sometimes my assessments aren't brutally honest. How painful is a standing long jump? However, there's some candor in it. It's like, "Oh, I am really lacking here, here and here."

Yes, you're lacking here, here and here. I believe your goal needs to be "not to be lacking in those areas."

Then, we fill in the blanks, and the rest doesn't take very long. It's like three weeks. All of a sudden, I'm a genius, and I always humbly joke that I agree.

The problem with the bulk of the population is that they know exactly where they are. They *know* their Point A.

As one woman told me, "I'm fat. My husband won't touch me."

These are honest assessments.

"I feel lousy. None of my clothes fit."

The problem is they don't have a Point B; it's more like they have a Point Z.

Every time I go to the grocery store, I see pictures of these three sisters who have a TV show. They all got started because their dad was a lawyer in a famous case. They had videos taken of themselves in acts that probably should be reserved for the marital bedroom. It's obvious there was a lot of work that had been done by physicians and surgeons.

I once saw an interesting thing by a 30-year-old singer who showed her before-and-after pictures after Photoshopping. Her legs are thinner. Her waist is thinner. Her boobs got bigger—all because of the magic of a camera and a computer.

The problem is, some people who are at Point A—I'm fat; my husband won't touch me—want to get to Point Z. They want to look like the girl who's on the magazine cover.

Well, that's just not reasonable. It's fine, but it's not reasonable. Maybe that's a great long-term goal.

I would applaud somebody who's going down that path. I would also argue that you need to be realistic about some things. But I support any and all goals.

Then there's a third category of people I have also been discovering more and more often. They don't know Point A, and they have no idea about Point B. They just plead, "Help me."

It reminds me of this girl I taught years ago. I was teaching a class called Sacred Scripture. She walked up after class, put her hands on her hips and said, "I just don't get it."

"What?"

She said, "This."

I said, "What's this?"

She said, "This class."

Oops. Why don't you pay attention? For an hour a day, five days a week, we do stuff. You would kind of get a clue after about week three or four.

There are those people who don't get "this." However, they still want my advice. I'll be at a party, and they'll want my hard-earned advice for which I charge bunches an hour. But they want it for free because we're at the Fritos bar together.

Why do I spend so much time talking about goals? It's because that line between Point A and Point B is going to be today, tomorrow, the next day and the day after. That line is going to be your food choices. It's going to be the workout decisions you're going to make.

Having said this, I've had great clarity over something. Steve Ledbetter and Rob Umfress helped me with this. I'm really proud about this thing called "the quadrants." Here's a quick overview of quadrants for dummies.

Quadrant One would be like junior high and high school PE classes. People in this quadrant need a lot of qualities that are very low level.

Quadrant Two is basically the collision sports and the collision occupations. They need a lot of qualities, and at a really high level. Trust me. You can meet a lot of high school football players and never see a future professional football player. Players need some pretty serious qualities to play in the NFL and NBA.

Every so often, you'll read a thing about how the Navy SEALs train. A bunch of guys will go to the gym that week and say, "I'm training like a Navy SEAL." Training like a Navy SEAL and being a Navy SEAL...there's a big difference.

Quadrant Three is where most people are—very few qualities at a reasonable level. A fat-loss client and a discus thrower are both Quadrant Three. As a discus thrower, you need excellent technique and a fair amount of strength. With fat loss, you need to adhere to a diet and probably do some type of inefficient movement that we call exercise.

Quadrant Four is basically only one or two qualities, but at a level that's extremely high. I usually think of the 100 meters or the deadlift for a deadlift specialist. If you're a 100-meter runner, speed is the thing you need. If you're a deadlifter, there are probably one, two or three things you need, but absolute bar-bending strength is going to take you a long way.

This quadrant idea is kind of my "invention," if you will, and I'm proud of it.

There are some problems in our fitness world today. The biggest problem is that every time you get a fitness magazine or every time you get on the internet and go to a fitness site, you get new ideas.

Quadrant One—that developmental time—is great for everybody. Everybody should have a Quadrant One phase. If you're trying to get back in shape and haven't trained in 20 years, I would love it if you decided to go back five days a week to a 7th grade PE class. You learn a new sport every day. You run two laps and do an obstacle course. After 186 days of that, you're going to be in okay shape. Then, spend the afternoons playing with your friends—playing tag, hide-and-go-seek and street football.

From Quadrant Four, I certainly wouldn't mind being a 100-meter runner. That would be pretty cool, but I don't think it's going to happen tonight.

Quadrant Two, mainly because of football and Special Forces, gets the most press.

Quadrant Three, where most people should be, has its own little set of problems.

Recently, I've come up with two concepts I'm pretty happy about.

Let's go to Quadrant Two, and let's talk about the issue. You have a lot of qualities, and you need to have all those qualities at a level that, honestly, most people can never get even one of them, but you need dozens of them at a high level. It comes down to two words for me. I call it "managing compromises."

I think about this all the time when I watch American football. We'll be watching a game. A fan will say, "You know what they ought to do? They ought to put in this play. Old 97. Just like what we used to do. Old Hennigan. He'd pitch me the ball and I'd flip it back there. Old Riley."

You almost want to sit down and say, "This is February, the day of the Super Bowl, and that's something that should've been done during July." The problem with your brilliant idea is somewhere between July and February.

I have great respect for a high school football program at De La Salle High School—the De La Salle Spartans. Coach Ladouceur has done some amazing things. One of the things I read about him was that he believes the best defense is an overwhelming offensive line.

His offensive linemen train year-round, practicing their first three steps so much so that when they play, it always seems like their offensive linemen are beyond the defensive line and the linebackers the instant the ball is snapped. I would love to be a running back for De La Salle because they'll gain five or six yards of carry just by literally falling forward on every play.

At De La Salle, they run an offense called the Veer. If De La Salle gets behind by 21 points in the third quarter, they're in trouble. Year in and year out, a 21-point switch is going to be hard to do with the Veer.

There's another offense called the System, which is a variation of the spread run by Mike Leach. In the System, the first thing the offensive linemen do is take three steps straight backward. Then they let the defensive linemen and linebackers do all their blitzes and all the things they want to do. They just protect their little area and man up as the players come past them.

The Veer has the offensive linemen going down three steps. The System has the offensive linemen stepping back three steps. If you're down by 21 points in the fourth quarter, the System might be a pretty good option, along with some luck and maybe a break or two.

However, you can't do the System *and* the Veer. For those of you who don't understand football, don't worry, although I do think you understand the principle.

To be a football coach, you have to learn to manage compromises. Since you can literally do everything, in Quadrant Two you have to realize *No, you can't.* Do you need flexibility work? Yes. Should you become as flexible as...? Sure, it would be nice to be as flexible as...

Do you see the problem?

Yes, you want to be flexible. Do you want to be strong? Yes, you want to get strong—every bit as strong as you can get. Should you work on your speed training? Yes, you should work on your speed training.

What about your endurance? You should run seven marathons back to back to back. Read *Born to Run* and run barefoot in the mountains of Mexico. That's exactly what you need to do.

First, the problem is there's only so much time in a day. Second, there's only so much time in a life. You're not going to get all this done.

What am I saying? I'm saying that in Quadrant Two, for those of you in collision sports and occupations, you have to learn to get used to this idea that you can certainly do a whole bunch of things, but you can't do everything optimally all the time.

That's managing compromises.

I've been working on this, and now there's a follow-up to this. For example, Napoleon came up with this idea called The Grand Strategy. The United States did it pretty well in World War II. Grand Strategy is this idea that, "Here's the issue. Here's the weakness. How are we going to focus on this weakness?"

As a high school football coach, you might go down to your sixth- and seventh-grade feeder programs and say to the coaches, "I want you to run the same program, do the same things we do, use the same terms we use. You don't have to do everything we do, but let's use the same language."

That's not a bad idea.

In the military, grand strategy is having the courage to see what might be your weakness. In the United States, one of the weaknesses we have as a country is that we have these massive oceans on both sides of us. It's possible for a submarine to pull up right next to us. You could probably sneak a submarine pretty close to San Francisco.

That's a problem. How do we manage that weakness?

I would say our extended Navy is pretty solid. That's how we do it. We're very good about those borders. Sadly, as I understand, it's the other borders that are a problem in this modern day and age, which is funny if you think about it historically.

Still in Quadrant Two, the next thing with managing compromises is strategy. This would be how to prepare for a season or a game. I always tell people, "Hide your issues."

Hide your weaknesses. Of course, in tactics, what you do on game day is attack *their* weaknesses or attack *their* issues.

If you have a five- or ten-year program to become the best fighter in the world, you really might want a solid step-by-step program addressing your weaknesses or your issues year by year. Of course, as you get close to a fight, you want to hide those issues. When you're in the ring, you just find out what Eddie's problems are and go after him. You wail on him.

In Quadrant Three, it's a little different. It's all about managing options. I always ask this question, although I know the answer: What diet works?

Here's what I know. From what I've read and from all my experience, every diet works. The diet you stay on works. The diet you do where you stay within the boundaries works.

What's the best training program? It's whatever you do that works.

We always joke in the strength field that the best program is what somebody else is doing. As a discus thrower, you need to get strong. There are discus throwers who have gotten very good by doing the power lifts—the bench, squat and deadlift. But there are other methods of getting stronger for the discus, like Al Feuerbach, who was a national champion in the Olympic lifts. That's pretty impressive. He was a very good Olympic lifter.

You can get strong doing strongman work. As I've also told people, there are plenty of Highland Games: Go to the Highland Games. Training for the Highland Games might be a great way to get ready to throw the discus farther.

If you did the three main kettlebell moves—the goblet squat, the getup and the swing—and then did just the bench press and the deadlift, you would probably have enough base of strength to be a great discus thrower if you had the courage to stick with it.

No one will ever do that, of course.

There's another option. What kind of technique do you have? Well, there's the Utah State wide-leg technique. There's the no-reverse technique. There's the John Powell tight-leg technique. And there are a few variations here and there. To be frank with you, choose one and stick with it.

Now as to fat loss, in the book *The 4-Hour Body*, Tim Ferriss documents that doing his slow-carbohydrate diet with three workouts of 75 swings three days a week gets fat off of people. That's not very much, but you missed the point: That's an option.

Stick to the slow-carbohydrate diet, and do some swings. Does it work? Yes, it does.

Do Atkins. Atkins works. My wife and I once did strict Atkins. I had never really worked my arms before. One day a week, I did front squats. One day, I did some military exercises. On two days a week, I did curls and triceps extensions. My guns got huge. I got my bodyweight down to 209 pounds doing that.

Then, of course, the Highland Games season shows up, and there's no way I can compete at 209 pounds. However, doing Atkins and working my guns worked for fat loss. In fact, I'm sitting here wondering, "Why don't you do that again, you idiot?"

When we look at Quadrant Three, we look at fat loss, among other things. Basically, what most adults do is Quadrant Three behavior.

Most of track and field is Quadrant Three. It's so simple. Track and field events are technique and strength. *How* you get strong is an option. There are lots of roads to the top of that mountain.

What about technique? In the long jump, there's the hang, the switch kick and probably small variations of those. That's maybe three choices. The really good British long jumper does the hang; he says it holds up better under the pressure of competition. He focuses on other things. That's genius. In other words, what I'm saying is if you're going to be a long jumper, take a technique and do that. Then, if you get strong, well, thank you very much.

The problem for those of us in Quadrant Three is that every time we open a magazine or the interwebz, all these new ideas show up. For two weeks, we're powerlifters. In three weeks, we become Olympic lifters. Then we try strongman. Then we do Highland Games.

We never optimize anything.

Here's an example—me. I tweaked my technique as a discus thrower day in and day out for my entire career, instead of choosing something, just sticking with it and mastering it. I'm not being critical of my career. I'm proud of it.

However, what you have to do as a coach and as a self-coached person if you're in Quadrant Three, is remind yourself that these are options. These are choices. You should choose one and follow it.

I've always been a big fan of things like the Atkins two-week induction diet and things like that. What's good about it is that it trains the brain that there are no options.

Here's an example of something we've known for a long time. There's a product called Purina Monkey Chow. It's a perfect food for humans. If I put you on an island with nothing but Purina Monkey Chow and water, you would survive.

It would be interesting to find out what your body would look like after two years living on an island on the Purina Monkey Chow diet—that's all you ate.

"Oh, Dan. Everything I eat just turns to fat."

Yeah? Eat nothing but Purina Monkey Chow for two years and tell me if it's true. I'm just thinking outside the box here.

What am I talking about? There are two things. First, take time always to really hash out your goal exactly. Then, shove the goal into one of the four quadrants—one, two, three or four. For most people, it's two or three. You want to be in a collision sport or you want to lose some pounds.

The second thing you always need to do is to really assess *exactly* where you are.

That's why I like before-and-after pictures so much, and why I like measurements. The scale can be a problem for some people. What does 200 pounds mean?

I like blood tests and, of course, I like those physical measurements, including the Functional Movement Screen. All this provides an idea of where you're starting. Once you know your Point A and have a vision of where Point B is, everything works.

Every diet works. Every training program works. They work for about six weeks.

My point is this: If you're a Quadrant Two collision person, there are so many qualities you have to master. You have to have the courage to say, "This is something we need to address. This is a weakness."

Mark Reifkind always says, "Train your weaknesses, but play with your strengths." There is some wisdom there.

For most of us who live in Quadrant Three, it's all about options. Every diet works. Stick with it. Almost any training program is going to be perfect for you. You just have to let it run its course. You have to follow both. Try not to flip from thing to thing to thing.

To summarize, figure out where you are. Assess where you are. Get a handle on where you are.

For most of us, and I'll just stick with Quadrant Three here, figure out a good, solid goal. Then, manage your options.

What other kind of diet or way of eating can you handle? What are the methods you've always followed well? If you're an intermittent faster and that works for you, then fast away.

If you're a "three protein shake and one meal a day" person, which is a phenomenal program for a lot of people, then do it.

If you're on Atkins, run with it. Stick with it for a while. Let it run its course. Try not to fall in love with every single thing you see that floats into your vision.

Sometimes when I talk, I'm told that I go in all kinds of circles, but I always get to the point.

My point is this: Assess, ask yourself what your goal is, and then learn to manage all options available to you.

Appendix 4

Fundamental Human Movements

I've been thinking a lot lately about the way we approach and teach movements. I've been concerned we've gotten ourselves into a situation where we've all started practicing this Frankenstein method, where the body is a collection of pieces.

But I like to teach the concept of a movement first. We can talk about the drills that support that concept and, finally, the pieces—the ankle, the knee, the butt.

For example, this thing called the "butt wink" that's shown up in discussions of squatting troubles me because the athlete is trying to see what you're saying, and we might just have a basic flaw in understanding what you're trying to say. So, I want to talk about my approach to the teaching of fundamental human movements.

Years ago, I was the editor of this fun little online newsletter called *Get Up*—the archives are on *danjohn.net,* along with some new issues. I started writing it when I broke my wrist in a couple of places. I found myself without an athletic career because my doctor was pretty clear that I'd never be able to lift again.

Two years later I had the best season of my life as a discus thrower, and after that I did really well in the Highland Games. I'm not saying my doctor was wrong. What I'm saying is, at the time I started writing *Get Up*, I began to learn some new ways of training, with some new ideas.

After our first edition, Mike Rosenberg said to me, "You need to put the mission statement of *Get Up* into the editions."

"That's great, but what's that?"

He says, "The things you believe in," and I said, "That's great. What are those?"

Thankfully, Mike and I were able to walk through the mission statement of *Get Up* and define my training system. It's three things.

First and foremost, *the body is one piece.* I got this from John Jerome's great book *Suppleness,* and, really—we're just one piece.

You are not a collection of parts. If you get the stomach flu, you probably are not going to squat well that day. If you think a certain lift is an upper-body lift, I'm going to poke a fork in your thigh and see if it really does affect it. You are one piece. You are one magnificent piece, and that's how you are. If you're ill, it's going to affect your training. If you broke up with your girlfriend, it's going to affect your performance. You're one piece.

Number two comes to us in several parts, but it will make sense in a minute: *There are three kinds of strength training—first, putting weight overhead; second, picking it up off the ground; and third, carrying it for time and distance.*

I think I've cleared this up a lot; I've clarified it. I've also expanded on it, which isn't always a good idea, but even today, I look at that list, and that's what we do. We put weights overhead.

We pick weights up off the ground. We carry weights for a while, and that's a pretty good training program.

The third point is that all training is complementary—not com-*pli*mentary, but com*ple*mentary. Com*pli*mentary would be, "You look very nice in your outfit today." Com*ple*mentary is, if you're training in sprinting in one part of your training program, you don't have to train it somewhere else; that's all you need. Working on something here carries over to there.

That overview article came out in July of 2002, and I still find it sound today. The problem recently has become this real growth in the Frankenstein belief. Watching some of my friends doing things or going to a workshop, they'll find this new way or this new drill, and they will spend way too much time working on whatever the new thing was.

Where we had something better before, it was just so simple we forgot to keep teaching it. As long as we can keep our brains away from Frankenstein for a while, I think we'll be okay.

As I think about Frankenstein, I also think about my friend Stuart McGill. Stu was the person who really clarified things for me when he looked at the way my body is structured and said I had a Celtic hip. Basically, the way I'm built makes me a good thrower. It allows me to quarter-squat a lot of weight but not deep-squat a lot of weight.

We are not all born the same. There are genetic differences. All you need to do to see this is sit down next to some NBA players. It's freakish because sitting next to them or across a table, you'll feel like you're about the same height they are. They'll stand up and you'll realize they're just built differently. They don't squat well, because, like my friend Walter at 7' 4", that bar has to travel a long way to the bottom.

If you can remember, we're not all built the same.

There are going to be differences. There are going to be differences in the way we're raised. There are going to be genetic differences. There are also going to be a whole lifetime of injuries and adaptations you're going to forget about. If you can keep that in the back of your mind the whole time someone is talking about movement, it will be a good place to start.

I'd like to add two words to coaching that really help us understand this whole idea of fundamental human movements and training everybody on planet Earth. The first word is this—*integrity.* We'll talk about integrity more in a moment. The other word is *environment.*

Integrity and environment—both of them are very important to understand.

The word "integrity" is a word that's used in moral theology. It's used in business relationships. It's used in life a lot, but it's also used in sports. "Integrity" in moral theology means being the same person in every situation. You'll hear something like, "Doing what is right even when it is difficult."

In strength training and in athletic performance, it's the understanding that the body is one piece, and this is probably the most important truth I know. You are one single person. When we train out there, when we go to the gym, you've got to understand we need to build YOU up—the whole system of you and every aspect of you—to either increase your athletic performance or simply to survive being mixed with this thing I call the "environment."

The "environment," in my language, is everything else. In the situation I'm in, it's the floor, the wall, or the ceiling. If I go outside, it's going to be nature—the trees, the grass, the concrete.

But it also can be your opponent.

If you're a discus thrower, your environment is pretty simple. It's going to be in a ring of cement that's just a bit over eight feet.

It's going to be the discus in your hand that you're about to get rid of. It is the wind. It could be your opponents, or it could be fans. It could be the noise over there, anything from a diesel engine to people fooling around in the crowd, but the environment for a discus thrower is pretty safe and sane.

If you're a football player—either soccer or American football—your environment can be insane. Your environment is with 21 other people running around. There's going to be a football. There are going to be officials. There are going to be lots of collisions. There's going to be a lot going on, and you're going to have a crowd.

If you're in battle in a war situation, your environment is going to explode geometrically from there. There are snipers. There are drones. There's a spy in the sky. There are landmines. There are also natural issues like snakes and tigers and all the rest.

There's also the enemy right across, but there are your own guys protecting you as well. There are tanks…all kinds of things. That's why battle is so stressful.

This is about being *you* in every situation, building up who you are, and then adapting to the environment.

Now we can talk about the fundamental human movements: the push, the pull, the hinge, the squat, loaded carries and what I call "the sixth movement."

Let's start with the basic, simple ones, and we'll build from there. Maybe it's because I'm an American or because I grew up in the great tradition of strength and health, but I always seem to start with the push. I've always thought the military press was the one-stop answer to all questions, but let's talk about this very simply; let's define the push a little differently from now on.

Let's define the push as separation from the environment—*separation from the environment.*

It's what you see with a baby almost instantly. I have two grandchildren as I write today. It's been interesting to watch them get on the floor and push the floor away—see something, push it. Push it. Push it. Push it. It's fascinating because as they age, they're going to push things away. It is the job of a teenager to push the family away. It is the job of people in their early 20s to push away early life and become adults.

When we talk about Vladimir Janda and his phasic muscles—the delts, the triceps, the abs and the glutes—these are the big pushing muscles. To summarize this in an interesting way, pushing seems to use the muscles of youth. We're trying to separate ourselves from the environment, so we can send ourselves to another environment.

Pull is the next one, and I have a different definition now for pulling. It's *embracing the environment,* but if you're a wrestler, your environment is your opponent. When you pull, you bring your opponent closer. It's what you see me do with my grandchildren. I want to hold them and cling to them.

As I age, I want to bring everything closer and closer back to me. I look at old yearbooks. I look at old pictures. I grab up old friends and hold them close. I don't want my children to grow up. I want to cling to them.

Pulling seems odd, but these muscles seem to be the muscles of aging. Again, Janda had this idea with his tonic muscles. These are the pecs, the biceps, the inner muscles of the thighs, the hip flexors and the hamstrings. These are all the muscles that pull the environment closer together.

I've changed things to the way I used to teach, to bring in the sixth movement... groundwork, usually. I'm now calling it "integrity with the environment."

It's being one person—one person—with the environment.

It has come to me, as I study this, that the problem most of us have is that we've become so isolated and separate from our environment. So much of good modern training is in the *Primal Moves* by Peter Lakatos and *Original Strength* from Tim Anderson. These are reminders to get back on the floor. Read Chip Conrad's work; learn his idea of getting back to crawling and lying on the ground doing groundwork.

For those of you in the martial-arts traditions, this is natural, but it's a lot more than that. It's all the rolling around on the ground, and it's all the getting up, but I also think there are two basic kinds. The first is what I call engaging the horizontal environment.

I know that sounds a bit too thick, but that's what crawling is. Crawling and getting down on the ground *is* engaging with the horizontal environment. Most of us would be well suited to get back on the ground for more and more of our training. Sadly, very few people are going to take that simple advice, but that's a big missing element from most people's training.

Watching my grandson, Danny, play in this little splash pond where he crawls in there and tries to stop the water from coming in and crawls away, you could wonder, is he bear crawling? Is he Spider Man crawling? I don't know, but I do know this: If you did exactly what he was doing for that hour in the splash area, you would be exhausted and probably pass out. It's difficult, but it's so valuable for all of us.

The next thing is a little different—it's to brachiate. This means engaging the vertical environment. Brachiators have opposable thumbs, have hypermobile shoulders and can do the monkey bars. If you're reading and you understand this, you are a brachiator, first and foremost.

We can easily bring these back into our culture by doing two very simple things. I think the monkey bars and rope climbing are the two easiest ways to bring them back in a gym setting, but honestly, climbing trees is what we're all about here. We need to bring back tree forts, which were a big deal when I was young. You rarely see them anymore.

When you combine the push, the pull and the sixth movement, these allow us to navigate the environment with the upper body. Crawling, you need your upper body engaged, and, if you're going to climb a tree, you'd better use your upper body. Even though it would be interesting to try to sprint up the side of a tree, good luck with old Mr. Gravity.

Crawling and brachiating are beginning to be rediscovered. It was something you would see quite a bit—it was very common back in PE when I was young and even more so in the 1940s and '50s. It's a rare school today that would have rope climbing as part of its education. To have a rope-climbing test is almost completely unusual, isn't it?

In school playgrounds you see as many monkey bars as you used to, but if you can get the kids back on those, that's a secret to a healthy, happy upper body for the rest of their lives. It's not complicated. Go to the park. Do your monkey bars. Climb some rope. Set up a rope in your backyard, and enjoy.

It bothers me that I missed the boat on the next thing I want to write about. In my recent work with Gray Cook, I was reminded about something that really changed my lifting career back in about 1991: loaded supports.

In 1990–1991, I was working with Dave Turner, and my lifts were improving day in and day out. It was just this nice time in my training life. We had a great facility at the Upper Limit gym—bumper plates, lots of platforms, lots of racks and lots of enthusiastic training partners, which really helped. Dave asked me, because I was struggling on a few things, to start adding loaded supports.

I would go into the rack, put a lot of weight on the bar and just lock my elbows out overhead, so I was doing only about a two-inch move. I was perfectly vertical, and I got up to a lot of weight. The other thing he asked me to do was quarter-squats with as much weight as I could possibly do, and just practice holding the position at the top of the rack position.

I had forgotten all about lockouts and supports. Those changed me as a weightlifter, because once you can quarter-squat 800 pounds, 315 pounds in the clean just isn't heavy anymore. It also teaches posture and support with a very simple concept, which is a vertical plank.

To help me understand the way the body works, I listen to Brett Jones. He once described the way we should sit as a "box on a bowl." The rib cage is a box, and the pelvic girdle is a bowl. If the bowl is sitting flat and no water is pouring out any of the sides, you can stick a box on top of that bowl, and that box will sit there for the rest of time. If you tilt that bowl in either direction, the box is going to have to make some kind of compensation. Otherwise, it's going to slip off. If you can get the pelvis to sit right, the rib cage and the whole body will rest quietly on the top.

I've noticed hip flexor stretches, goblet squats and swings all seem to help, but Gray showed me something that seems to instantly fix this pelvis position. At our gym, we call it a "kneeling plank." Get on both knees. Have your knees spread wide enough—in about the same position your feet would be when you squat. Sit up as tall as you can. The top of your head drives the zenith.

Position your belt parallel to the floor. Dig your toes in, and then one small other thing: Behind your back, I want you to hold some kind of load, like a kettlebell. Relax and let the load pull you down. You're on your knees. You have a load behind your back.

You're holding onto it, and you're driving the top of your head to the zenith.

By the way, don't ask for a video on how to do it. It's isometric. There's no movement. Hold this as long as you can and then gently bring the weight to the floor.

The mistake most people make is this butt-back position, where they let all of the load sit on their quads, on their thighs. To fix it, don't do anything. Let the people sit there in that loaded position until the quads get tired; they will slowly push the pelvis in line. The beltline will come parallel to the floor.

They will relax and suddenly say, "My hip flexors are so tight." That's the sign they're doing it right.

It's very simple. It teaches us the box and the bowl positions. That's a good way to look at this whole exercise. From this, I have moved on to teaching the whole hip movement in a different way now.

I'm going to come back and repeat the same information I always do: The squat is not a swing, and the swing is not a squat. The hip moves maximally whether it's hinging or squatting, but in the hinge, there's only minimal knee movement, and, in the squat, there's maximal knee movement.

It's great to say that, and I've said it 100 times, but it doesn't always translate to what people are trying to do, so I've come up with something called the "Hip Instruction Trinity." I'm trying to get experienced and inexperienced trainees to really learn this basic human truth. It's the three exercises—the kneeling plank, the six-point rock, which I got from Tim Anderson, and the hip thrust, which is now also known as the pelvic tilt or the supine bridge.

These three exercises, done either in a circuit or just as a teaching, instructs people once again how to squat and how to hinge. The interesting thing is, the kneeling plank is the top movement for both the squat and the hinge. I strived for a long time trying to piece these two positions together and I couldn't. Finally, the kneeling plank from Gray Cook teaches us this.

In the pelvic tilt, I always have people put the backs of their hands on the ground so the shoulders and the chest open up and drive those thumbs down. It's just a small thing we do. That's all the pelvic tilt is. That would be the pelvic tilt as a plank.

Next is the kneeling plank from Gray.

The third movement is called the "six-point rock." All we're doing in this position is getting on six points—hands, knees, feet, holding our chest up like we're squatting, and then slowly sinking back and forth, back and forth into a deep rocking movement like a squat. I always argue this: If you have a client who can do a six-point rock but cannot squat, the issue is load—not the movement.

What's nice about these three movements is these can be warmups. They can be cooldowns. They can be done between sets. They can be done on the road. They can be done anywhere in the world, by yourself, in a hotel room, on a beach, and you can practice the most important thing you can do in your life, which is using the hips.

Once you master using the hips, great things happen in sports.

Kneeling planks solved the hip-displacement continuum for me. I had known for a long time that the swing is not a squat and the squat is not a swing. I knew that, but the problem was that, at the top of that continuum, it would always be "blank."

What I want you to think is the kneeling plank is the top of this continuum. That is the place where you're going to have this instant where the squat and the hinge come back together again.

I believe you should always consciously try to build up your hinge. If that's through swings, you would do more repetitions with a heavier bell. With deadlifts, you would do a heavier weight, but you always maintain your squat.

You want that squat to be as elegant as you can over your entire life.

Let's make sure we're clear on this. Hinges and squats both have maximal hip movement, but one big difference. When you hinge the hips—that's swings and jumps—it means *maximal* hip movement and *minimal* knee movement.

Squats are both maximal hip movement and maximal knee movement, which is why the swing is not a squat and the squat is not a swing. When people's lower backs are hurting from doing kettlebell swings, almost universally it's because they're trying to squat their swings.

Next, carries. The concept for loaded carries is very simple. It's integrity under load. The problem with coaching people in the farmer walk is that all you do is have them pick up something and walk. That's really all the coaching you'll ever have to do.

When you're doing carries, you're going to have the top of your head driving the zenith. You're going to have your shoulders down. You're going to have your chest up. You're going to strive to keep your pelvis underneath your rib cage, because if you don't, the weight is going to rip you apart.

One of the things I always tell people is, with the loaded carries, the skill is the drill and the drill is the skill. After the farmer walks, where you have a weight in both hands, I progress people to the suitcase carry. That's where you have a weight in only one hand, hanging down.

From here, there are all kinds of other walks we can do. They're all easy to learn. They're easy to teach. There might be no better way to teach work capacity than those movements. We'll get back to that in just a minute.

If you understand loaded carries and the sixth movement, you understand integrity.

Walking to carries to sprinting (unloaded) reflect the hunter-gatherer historic record. In the hunter-gatherer idea, we spent a lot of time in our prehistoric period walking around. Anything we wanted to move from here to there, we had to carry and if we got hungry enough, we had to sprint and chase something down. Sometimes we were also dinner and had to sprint and get out of the way.

I think walking, loaded carries and sprinting are the natural way to do locomotion. Sometimes we have to jump. That's hinges with a lot of acceleration. Here in Utah, that might be when you see a rattlesnake. They're pretty common up in certain areas. It's nice to be able to leap up, leap over and leap on things maybe to save your life or to just change positions.

Sometimes, you'll want to throw things. My definition of throwing is pretty simple. It's integrity with acceleration.

One of the things I'm proud of is that years ago, I figured out that doing loaded carries, especially the farmer walk and the suitcase carry, really helped our throwers throw farther. It certainly helped me in 2004, when I had probably the best season of my life.

My point here is that loaded carries teach integrity—*being one piece*. When you're trying to throw something fast, you need to be one piece with long arms and long hands and all the rest. Loaded carries support that concept.

In our thrower's language, we have certain words we use a lot. For example, throwers are "built from the ground up." That's a common coaching phrase, a common concept. You look at a thrower, and you start with the ground—the feet, the ankles, the knees—and you work your way up.

Coach Maughan had a funny way of saying this. He would say, "If your brains were in your feet, you'd throw a lot farther."

A very famous way to explain the throwing motion is that "the arms come last and fast."

When you're a thrower, one of the things you learn is you've got to throw with your whole body, and yet at the same time, you've got to whip that implement, no matter what the implement is. You have to have integrity with acceleration. Throwing is a full-body movement.

A lot of people ask about one last thing: What about abs?

This is important. There is an American shot putter by the name of Dane Miller. He's a very fine thrower. He came up with an interesting formula about throwing: $A+B+C=D$. Let's just say that "A" is the upper body, "B" is the lower body, the abs are "C," and performance is "D."

We all know, as throwers, if you build your legs up, you tend to throw farther. If you work your upper body and you get your bench up, you might not throw farther. You might. You might not. You never know.

The interesting thing is "C." If you stop working your abs or you stop training your abs, very often, performance drops.

Dane was the person who put this together for me. By themselves, training your abs won't necessarily help you throw further, but if you drop them, it will hurt your performance. They're kind of an odd little missing gap.

As I've always said, your core should be considered like a chain link fence—very strong, but extremely flexible. If you think about your abdominal area, it has to do four basic things. Most of it is preventing you from leaning over too fast, leaning back, getting pushed side-to-side against your will.

That's where our little family of things called the loaded carries come in because their job is to teach your body, especially with the suitcase carry—the one-handed farmer walk—to stay in one piece under asymmetrical load.

The more I've been working on this, I've come to some interesting insights. Let's talk about the two big ones.

Three movements tend to be the best movements for hypertrophy. They are, of course, the push, the pull and the squat. I can't think of an image of bodybuilders where you don't have them rowing, pressing and squatting. These are the muscles of hypertrophy.

The problem many of us have is we get too caught up in push-pull-squat, push-pull-squat, push-pull-squat. You can look good—push-pull-squat. You can look very good—push-pull-squat.

The downside is that after nothing but push-pull-squat, once you try to move, leap or sprint after something, of course, you pull a hamstring.

This leads us to the next two ideas. These are the two that seem to build explosiveness and work capacity: hinges and loaded carries.

We've been doing experiments here at the gym with farmer walks and we're trying to come to a number that gives the threshold of when you're strong enough from loaded carries.

We've come to this idea—we're using yards instead of meters, but that's just because of our audience here in Utah. What we decided on was a bodyweight farmer walk, and there are a couple of ways to do this. You could do a trap bar with your bodyweight on it or farmer walks with half-bodyweight in each hand. Your job is to pick that up and walk it for distance.

We've discovered about 100 yards is the threshold where you're at a good place in your work capacity. Let's just say it that way: You have enough. We can certainly build more on it, but less than that means we need to get you stronger, so you can deadlift your bodyweight and, secondly, have some kind of endurance so you can handle a 100-yard walk.

We've tested only men so far, but when I worked at Judge Memorial, we found the female athletes could pick up 85 pounds per hand and go for a long distance. For whatever reason, women are better at loaded carries than men are, especially if we go by percentage. They just seem to be naturally built to take loaded carries easier and smoother.

The hard thing, of course, is convincing some women to do loaded carries.

Loaded carries and hinges build work capacity. We know this from the 10,000-swing challenge. We know this from the farmer walk work we're doing. We are working on two ways of measuring this—work capacity and its twin, which is explosiveness.

Very simply, we're using the standing long jump to measure explosiveness. You should be able at any time in your life to do a standing long jump the distance of your height.

It's a pretty simple little tool we've been using: We expect you to jump your height.

Now as a six-footer, if I go up against elite discus throwers, many elite discus throwers sneak up on 10 and 11 feet. If I'm only jumping six feet, my problem is I've done what's expected, but I still don't have the explosiveness needed to be an elite discus thrower.

We have a way of measuring work capacity, which is the farmer walk, and I think we have a method of measuring explosiveness, which is the standing long jump.

What's great about both of these is that they are easy to teach. The standing long jump—it's pretty simple to teach that, and the farmer walk, you pick it up and go.

But, the upside is this: If you improve on those two things, you've shown improvement.

That's a easy sentence to say. If you improve, you've improved. People don't, out of nowhere, increase the standing long jump very often. There has to be a reason for the increase. I'd like to think after six weeks, it was our six weeks of training. If your work capacity goes up, I have to assume it's those six weeks of training we did.

I'm excited about this work. What we're doing with our basic human movements is to try to change the way I explain the concepts of each.

Let's review the concepts: push—separation from the environment; pull—embracing the environment.

There are two ideas to the sixth movement, which is integrity with environment, and we have two kinds. We have crawling, which is engaging the horizontal environment and, of course, brachiating, which is engaging the vertical environment.

It's very simple and easy to put crawling into a normal workout. Do some bear crawls or roll around on the ground. Do some tumbling. Do some cartwheels and you're fine.

Brachiating in some situations can be a little bit tougher to set up, but I've had someone tell me they've been practicing brachiating on a simple pullup bar by doing kind of "one hand on, the other hand on," left hand, right hand, left hand, right hand. I thought that was clever and interesting.

The concept for squatting is what I've been using for years. The body sits between the legs. The body is not built on top of the legs. The body slides between the legs.

Loaded carries are integrity under load, and our throws are integrity with acceleration.

Then we add the loaded supports, which you might be confused by until you actually try doing Gray Cook's kneeling plank.

I'm trying to re-teach and re-think the way I approach the fundamental human movements. Instead of getting stuck on the

Frankenstein—if you have a problem with the squat, for example, "Oh, you have tight ankles"—I get you back to the concept.

The concept is this: *This is the vision of the swing. This is the vision of the hinge. This is the vision of the loaded carry.*

From there, we can work on some drills. We can teach drills, but very often, and here's my point, people already know how to do them. Our teaching actually holds them back from doing the movement.

If you're going to teach a loaded carry like the farmer walk, and you talk about the feet and the ankles and the knees and the hips and the grip, all that talking gets people away from doing that set of farmer walks perfectly the first time.

This idea changed the way I teach everything. Start with the concept, and then move to the drill. If that doesn't work, then we move to Frankenstein—stretching the ankles, putting a band around the knees, cracking hips, talking about the shoulders, talking about the wrists.

It's different and it's unusual, but it's our tradition.

Appendix 5

Armor Building

THERE ARE A LOT OF REASONS most people don't succeed at their physical goals. I have thought for a while that the number-one reason is simply that they're trying to do everything all the time. I'll get a question about mass building and will recommend lots of squats, lots of food and lots of rest. The follow-up question from the same person will usually include something about six-pack abs, agility work and dunking a basketball.

This is too much!

Much of the confusion comes from the fact that I basically use one tool—the barbell and all of its close cousins like kettlebells, dumbbells and the like—to help you accomplish your goals from fat loss and muscle gain to mobility and flexibility.

For most people, I argue that we need to find periods in the year, usually from three to six weeks and perhaps as long as eight weeks, to work hard on specific qualities. I think the Velocity Diet is amazing for fat loss, but it would be hard to do it while also at an NFL training camp. It doesn't mean the Velocity Diet is good or bad, nor does it mean that being in camp is right or wrong, as this is not moral theology.

And this is precisely the thought process that destroys most people:

Trying to do or be everything all the time

There are times to burn fat, build muscle, get more explosive and prep for a sport, but it's nearly impossible to do this all the time. And there are some qualities that you should ONLY work for a little while and ONLY when you need it.

I work with a lot of people in the collision sports and collision occupations. One of the hardest things to prepare for these endeavors is what we call "armor building." This is a term one of my football players coined a few years ago. Basically, he felt that some of the exercises we were doing, specifically in his case the thick-bar curl and the double-kettlebell front squat, were helping him be a better running back.

It gave him a feeling "like armor."

At first, I didn't understand what he meant. I assumed he meant like firepower.

A few years ago, I worked with a high school running back, Tony N, who had a coach who didn't believe in weightlifting. The coach probably didn't like those new-fangled automobiles, either.

After a few sessions of working with him, he found that doing what he called "The Exercise," a combination of power snatches and overhead squats, gave him some tools on the field that no one else had. In his last five football games his senior year, Tony ran for more than 200 yards each game.

But, that's not armor—that's not what we are talking about here. We're talking about the ability to handle collisions and contact.

When I wrestled in high school, I would spend the first week or so stuffing wet toilet paper up my nose, as it bled every session. Magically, around week two, that very same forearm to the face wouldn't cause a drop of blood to come out. Frank Shamrock, the great fighter, called this "callusing," and it's the first cousin to armor building.

Armor building is a focused attempt to prepare the athlete for contact. True, there will be some callusing, but the training will also include specific movements to gear up for collisions. Strangely, most of the athletes I have do this program note that they also look better in the mirror.

In a sense, armor building is a kind of bodybuilding for sport.

The most basic moves might also be the most exhausting. Every football player should have some intense loathing for grass drills, which are also known as "up-downs."

The coach has a whistle, and the job is to run in place, driving your knees high. When the coach blows the whistle, you throw yourself to the ground and leap right back up and into running in place. The running in place, as you soon discover, is the easy part.

Grass drills alone can prepare you for many things. Late in my high school football career, I realized that of all the things we did for conditioning, most had no carryover to the games. But, as much as I hated them, grass drills seemed to be "game like."

Football, rugby and war are very much about getting on the ground as fast as you can and then getting back up. I can remember one of my teammates complaining about practice and especially up-downs. He was a star in middle school and was learning that getting to puberty first was great, but you still had to keep working. I noticed that all the guys who never played felt that the hard work was a waste of time.

If you don't have a high school football coach around to guide you, try just rolling. I am a firm believer that tumbling and rolling is the missing link for most people's training.

Tim Anderson has been writing a lot lately on how simple rolling resets the body.

I know this: One of the great fears of adulthood is to say, and here comes the advertisement, "I've fallen and I can't get up." I am proactive about just about everything and would rather practice falling and getting up.

My standard "do this" basic rolling sequence (aka tumbling training) is this:

> *Five somersaults (forward rolls)*
>
> *Five right shoulder rolls*
>
> *Five left shoulder rolls*
>
> *Four ninja rolls (right shoulder roll, left shoulder roll, right, left)*
>
> *Bear crawl*
>
> *Three cartwheels facing one direction*
>
> *Three cartwheels facing the other*

And, finally, as I always joke, run to the bucket. For whatever reason, tumbling seems to affect the tummy at first. Think of it as a lousy diet program, too.

For many, grass drills and tumbling tossed into some training weeks once or twice a year might be a fun jumpstart to a fat-loss program or even a nice way to keep the motor running toward the end of a serious ripping program.

One of the reasons I like the Turkish getup so much is that it's a kind of *tai chi* grass drill or tumbling session. Rarely do I see the typical fitness enthusiast touch the ground, save for planks, and even that exercise seems to wane in popularity.

Remember the axiom: If no one in a typical gym is doing something, it's probably pretty hard to do. Rolling around on the floor doing getups is an insightful, thoughtful way to reorient you with getting off the ground.

And, as you age, learning to catch a fall, recover and get back up might be the secret to a more vigorous old age. Trust me: You will get older nearly every year.

With the barbell, there are several great armor-building moves. As I noted before, the thick-bar curl has been one of my odder go-to movements for the past few years. I am not sure what it does to the forearms, elbows and guns, but try them.

I use both actual fat bars and those thick grips that mimic the metal. Your budget will decide which way you go on this decision. Thick bars are expensive, but the curl and deadlift movements are stunning to do with them. The thick-bar curl can be done for reps up to 10, but usually I notice I just simply fail as the reps go up.

Whatever the reason, this exercise seems to get the body ready to take a hit.

The snatch-grip deadlift and the duck-stance deadlift—heels together, toes out—seem to also help the collision athlete. I have been thinking that this compromised position tends to wake up more of the system, especially the connective tissue. I have gone heavy with snatch-grip deadlifts in my career, and then soon I always seem to be able to take a whack or two. Correlation or causation is never too important to me because these two movements will quickly tax you, and we won't need a deep philosophy discussion after doing them.

For squatting, I hate the Zercher squat. Hate it. It kills me, but I have always noticed that my human inner tube seems much more powerful after doing these. This is that odd internal pressure—talk to a martial-arts person for details. Holding the bar in the crook of the elbow is callusing for the ages.

I have also experienced, as have Pavel and many other brighter people than me, that the Zercher squat demands a kind of moving mobility that has to be experienced to understand. If you hate Zerchers, you are probably doing them right.

With kettlebells, I have a one-stop shop for you: double-kettlebell cleans and front squats. I have this funny challenge:

> *One double-kettlebell clean and one double-kettlebell front squat*
>
> *Two double-kettlebell cleans and two double-kettlebell front squats*
>
> *Three double-kettlebell cleans...and you see where this is heading.*

The challenge is this: Go all the way up to 10 and 10 with the 24-kilo 'bells (32s if you're serious) without putting the 'bells down.

So far, no takers!!!

Here you go:

> *Grass drills*
>
> *Tumbling*
>
> *Getups*

Thick-bar curls

Duck-stance deadlifts

Snatch-grip deadlifts

Zercher squats

Double-kettlebell cleans and front squats

Beware of each of these, as they all bring forth an odd kind of soreness. The reps and sets have to be open ended. Honestly, without a coach blowing a whistle at you, it's going to be tough to push through some of this.

I think you can do armor building for about three weeks.

Generally, week one should emphasize getups and some tumbling. In the weightroom, try a few simple moves. Obviously, you should be fine-tuning your conditioning and basic technical skills, too. If you're a sport athlete, you should spend the bulk of your time prepping for the season.

Week one

Monday

General warmup

Getups

General orientation into the tumbling moves (practice!)

Double-kettlebell cleans and front squats (practice!)

Tuesday

General warmup

Snatch-grip deadlift practice

Zercher squat practice

Thick-bar curls

Wednesday

General warmup

Getups

General orientation into the tumbling moves. Try doing a basic rolling sequence (see above)

Double-kettlebell cleans and front squats. Try getting to 5 + 5

Thursday

Sports practice only

Friday

General warmup

Getups

General orientation into the tumbling moves. Try doing a basic rolling sequence (see above)

Double-kettlebell cleans and front squats. Strive for two sets of 5 + 5

Saturday

General warmup

Duck-stance deadlifts (practice)

Snatch-grip deadlifts

Thick-bar curls

Week two

Monday

General warmup

Getups

Duck-stance deadlifts

Snatch-grip deadlifts

Zercher squats

Thick-bar curls

Tuesday

General warmup

Tumbling

Double-kettlebell cleans and front squats. Try to get beyond 5 + 5.

Grass drills

Wednesday and Friday

Repeat Monday

Saturday

Repeat Tuesday

Week three

Monday

General warmup

Tumbling

Double-kettlebell cleans and front squats

Grass drills

Tuesday

General warmup

Getups

Duck-stance deadlifts

Snatch-grip deadlifts

Zercher squats

Thick-bar curls

Wednesday and Friday

Repeat Monday

Saturday

Repeat Tuesday

Now, you may ask where your beloved bench press is in this program—or whatever your heart desires that is missing. Well, add it in!

Or, as I usually suggest, leave it out.

This is only three weeks, and we are trying to use our valuable time to literally toughen the skin and body for contact.

Even if you are not a collision athlete, there is still a lot of value in trying some of these lifts and moves. From a fat-burning perspective, you are going to have a hard time finding movements more compelling than grass drills and tumbling.

With the odd barbell moves, you are going to discover the simplicity of the basic deadlift and squat when you return to them.

Here is the lesson: When it's time to kick it up a notch, you need to take a few weeks aside and really attack it. If you need to get some calluses and some armor, take some time to do it before you need it.

Appendix 6

Anaconda Strength

BACK IN THE EARLY 1960S, Gyula Zsivótzky walked across a field. According to my assistant college coach, Kevin Brady, at that moment, he realized something:

He would never be an elite athlete.

Kevin noted, "This guy walked like the greatest athlete I had ever seen."

Gyula, world record holder and Olympic gold medalist, simply walked across a field better than most of us will ever attempt. His training reflected the age: He lifted, he ran, he did gymnastics, he Olympic lifted and he trained like an athlete.

In a discussion on his training, he once gave us the secret:

We humans are like bicycle inner tubes: Our performance depends on our "inner pressure."

Sadly, most of us ride around on underinflated tires. True, the world looks at our treads first, but what really counts is the pressure.

I call this "anaconda strength." You might ask why, but just remember that I love stupid names that are hard to forget: slosh pipe, goblet squat, Hungarian core blaster and Bulgarian goat-bag swing.

True, the last one never caught on.

For the record, don't mistake this for "armacondas." The armacondas (patent pending) are my upper arms. Women demand to be squeezed in them, and men run screaming from my "flex-ability."

Mastering this internal pressure is the secret to some athlete movements. In the Highland Games, the caber toss dominates the photo streams. I once grabbed an 18-foot 185 caber and stood up. The wind up at the top of the caber is not like the wind on the ground: The caber's top would pop, move and heave with the breeze, and the crowd wondered why I just stood there.

Truth is…I couldn't move. When the top of the caber moved, the bottom leaped away, too. Handling that is anaconda strength.

It's not upper-body push, quad-dominant or hip hinge: It's squeezing everything to hold everything in place. I was locked to the ground, then…I took one step.

This is a missing link in everyone's training, along with loaded carries and squatting deep.

How do you know if you are missing it? Can you deadlift double bodyweight? Walk with bodyweight in each hand? Make a catch over the middle, get hit sideways by a linebacker, crash to the ground and then pop up and ask, "That's all you got?"

There are traditional lifting movements that build this internal pressure. In the last appendix, we discussed "armor building." It seems to build the skill of taking a hit either from an opponent or the ground. The short list:

Tumbling (especially the more aggressive martial-arts rolls and cartwheels)

Snatch-grip deadlifts

Zercher squats and Zercher deadlifts (the second demands a lot of flexibility)

Double-kettlebell cleans

Thick-bar work, including deadlifts and curls

One of my athletes, a national-level shot putter, noted that the snatch-grip deadlift is the secret to mastering the rotational shot put. "It feels like the throw."

If you throw, you know what he means.

Rack work can help, too. Few people do isometric work anymore, but there are three movements that teach this internal tension:

Press lockout

Squat lockouts

Deadlift lockouts

Go to the top position of each of the movements. Set the bar in a rack about one inch from the top. Now, load the barbell up. You will be shocked at how much you can load. It might be double your normal max.

It might take a while to get there, but as you load heavier and heavier, you will find that internal pressure building up and up. This is anaconda strength.

Small side story: Back during the height of the Vietnam War, I had several friends explain that this technique also taught them to artificially raise their blood pressure so they would get the designation "4-F." Another short life lesson for you there.

Be careful on the lockouts. Be sure to use a rack and some common sense. Hell, common sense is the rarest commodity in life.

The best way to train anaconda strength is using the family of loaded carries. The single best subset is the bag-carry family.

Bags are easy to come by: Find a field pack and add load to it. Some have used wood chips; others go to hardware stores and add washers or bolts. Don't add nails or screws (that won't make sense until you try these).

Eighty pounds is about the best weight for most uses. I also use water-softener bags that weigh 40 pounds each. You can load up to 120 pounds without a lot of hassle, but if they break, it becomes a real issue.

The best training tool is to bear hug the load and walk away. You can quickly feel the odd breathing pattern that you need in order to walk and hug at the same time.

A great follow-up to this is "bear-bear." Bear crawl for 50 yards, grab the bag, go for another 50. You can mix this into a few rounds of work with a partner doing "I go/you go" (I bear crawl while you bear hug, and then we switch), and make a training session of it.

To up the intensity and the feeling of internal pressure, add a sled. Put the sled on first, then grab the bag and try to "sprint" away. Tomorrow, let me say this to you:

"Those are your hamstrings."

By the way, this is the easiest way to mimic the value of hill work. The downside of hills is the fact that you get to the top. Then what? With sleds, the whole world is a hill.

Walking forward with a sled works the hamstrings; walking backward with a sled is great quad workout, especially the area around the knees. It's leg extensions without the embarrassment of using a machine.

To go up to the next step, which we call "juggernauts," is to combine the bag and the sled with a loaded backpack.

You can load a backpack with just about anything. I have a quality backpack into which we can load a 32-kilo kettlebell or other light bags. To do a juggernaut, you probably want to put on the backpack first. Then, pop the sled around your waist, and pick up the bag.

Now, sprint away.

This is what throwing the caber feels like on a hot, sunny day. This movement will teach you anaconda strength. This will make you strong in those weird ways that you see in superior athletes.

Like a hammer thrower walking across a field.

The Litvinov Workout

AN AMAZING THING HAPPENED in 1983—I went on a date. Okay, that was a joke, because everybody knows that during the '80s, I was covered with black-and-blue marks from being touched with 10-foot poles.

Actually, what really happened was the world championships of track and field began in Helsinki, and the list of winners is a "who's who" of sport. You'd find the names of Carl Lewis, Mary Decker, Edwin Moses and Sergei Bubka littered among the gold-medal winners.

It was also the year of an important failure. John Powell, who'd led American discus throwing for a decade, failed to make the finals. Powell came away with two important lessons, and, from his observations, he inspired a generation to rethink training for competition.

The discus trials were at nine in the morning. Powell had never trained—ever—to throw at nine in the morning. He thought he could just walk out and throw the qualifying distance. He learned after the competition that it took him a lot of time in the morning to get the same snap that he had in the mid-afternoon.

This is a good lesson for a lot of us who take performance for granted in life and sports.

When Powell looked around to see how the rest of the world was training, he noticed that his training hadn't advanced much, if at all. He noted that the throwers from the rest of the world were leaner, faster and more muscular.

Especially impressive was the young gold medal winner in the hammer, Sergey Litvinov. If you are interested in becoming leaner, faster and more muscular, keep reading.

From Powell's observations of Litvinov, I put together some training ideas that completely reshaped my approach to training athletes, and in turn, reshaped my athletes. It's such a simple training idea that you may discount it at first.

Let's start by looking at what Sergey Litvinov was doing that awoke Powell's imagination. It's truly a simple workout. Litvinov, a 5' 10", 196-pound hammer thrower, did the following training session:

> *Eight reps of front squats with 405 pounds, immediately followed by a 75-second 400-meter run. Repeat this little combination for a total of three times and go home, thank you.*

Wait. Let's stop here and marvel at what Powell observed. A 196-pound man front squatted 405...eight times!

"Dan, do you have any advice for my quad development?"

"Dear Reader: Front squat 405 eight times. I'll now debit your account for this expensive advice."

Moreover, Sergey racked the bar and ran 400 meters...then did this two more times.

After listening to Powell's story, I invented a workout combining front squats with running. Let's look at the basic workout, the Litvinov.

The Litvinov workout

Perform any big lift, and then drop the bar (gently) and run. My charges and I have used the following lifts:

> *Cleans*
>
> *Clean and press*
>
> *Clean and jerk*
>
> *Deadlift*
>
> *Front squat*
>
> *Overhead squat*
>
> *Snatch*

You can use any and all variations of snatches and swings with kettlebells and dumbbells.

Over time, we discovered the 400 was far too long a run for the needs of my athletes. I found that strength athletes weighing in the mid-200-pound range just didn't recover very well from the full 400. But, if you really desire a fat-loss blast, by all means run the 400!

Now, I have to ask myself: If the world champion weighs 196 and my chubby little body weighs 260, how does that extra 64 pounds help?

The devil is in the details with this workout. Back squats don't work because racking the weight and running away involve way too much care and planning. We also discovered that even our lightest racks were a hassle to pack into the bed of a pickup truck and haul to a place where we could combine the lifting and running.

Also, I hated leaving my bar, weights and rack outside in lousy weather collecting rainwater and mud. Plus I got tired of burning my hands on the hot plates in the summer sun.

Some lifts don't work very well, either. Yes, we tried other lifts, like military presses and one attempt with the bench press, but it seemed foolish—lots of work and set-up for not much of a return on the time and effort. The clean and jerk never seemed to work right, either. The lift has to be simple and easy to push quickly with little mental effort.

The best lifts are:

> *Front squat*
>
> *Overhead squat (if you're good at them)*
>
> *Snatch*
>
> *Swings with kettlebells or dumbbells (but really knock up the reps; try doing more than 30)*
>
> *The LitviSprint*

Soon, the Litvinov became re-imagined as the "LitviSprint." As we played with lifts and distance, we found ourselves one day with a kettlebell and a hill. We soon discovered that the speed and intensity of the run made a bigger impact on the workout than the lift itself.

Kettlebell swings followed by a hill sprint of 30 yards left us burning oxygen for hours after the workout. Moreover, massive amounts of meat and analgesic liquids (beer) did little to revive us.

Once again, the most obvious lesson of my coaching life had been reinforced: The more intense you can train, the better.

Yep, you knew that. So did I. Why, then, don't we follow the rule?

A nice little spin-off benefit began to emerge from the LitviSprints: If the athlete is learning a lift—very often the overhead squat—doing the sprint after the lift seems to speed up the learning process.

Why?

I have two ideas:

1—When most people try to learn a new skill, they think too damn much.

I'll try to show someone how to snatch or clean at a clinic, and the questions just keep coming.

"Where do I put my thumbs?"

(Um, near your fingers.)

"Where do I put my elbows?"

(Between the upper and lower arm.)

In making the new lift even more complex by adding sprints, the athlete stops with the questions and just does it. By magic, it looks "okay."

2—Moreover, they attempt perfection on the new skill the first time they try it.

I've probably squatted near 100,000 reps, and I still learn new things each time I read a Dave Tate article. Ain't gonna happen on the first set, people. The challenge of sprinting seems to get the athlete to forget perfection and focus on completion.

There's a lot to be said for this workout:

> *Bring one piece of equipment outside, or if you're lucky and have a gym with a nice area to sprint next to your*

> *weights, just get going. You'll get an unusually demanding workout with a minimum of mental effort.*

And this is the interesting part: As you finish the lift and attempt to sprint away, you'll instantly understand how well this workout will impact your overall conditioning. Usually, the first two steps feel like running in waist-deep water as the legs send up this response, "Could someone please tell us what the hell is going on?"

I contend that this combination is the single best crossover training idea ever to move from the weightroom to the sports arena. Athletes who do LitviSprints note the improvement on the field, track and court within a few workouts. Something is different, and performance improves.

LitviSleds

Not content with leaving well enough alone, I began experimenting with "LitviSleds." There are some equipment issues here: Beyond the bar or kettlebell or dumbbell and the need for an area to run, you'll also need a sled and a harness.

First, choose the lift you'll be performing before you start dragging the sled. I'd cut the list down to these simple moves:

> *Front squats*
>
> *Overhead squats*
>
> *Swings with kettlebell or dumbbell*

The reason you have to simplify is that you hook yourself up into the harness before you lift. You're hooked to the sled when you lift so you can drop the bar and sprint to drag away.

A caveat: Lift to the side of the path of the sled. Obvious, yes, but more than a few people have started their sprint or drag, snagged the weights and got yanked back to the ground.

It's funny to watch, but it may also really hurt you. I'll still laugh at you, but you will be hurt.

I have no idea how much you should load on the sled. I've found that hooking a 70-pound kettlebell so it drags is about right for most people. The drag is nice, but don't overdo it like many who think they need to pull a building.

What's important isn't wallowing around like a pig in slop but flying away like an athlete. Think, "Less wallow, more speed."

I also encourage you to go for about five seconds and not worry about distance. Otherwise, you lose the quality of effort almost immediately.

Summary

Litvinovs, LitviSprints and LitviSleds come from a very simple idea. The quality of effort is far more important than the quantity—a concept that'll be missed by many. Don't do 25-pound squats, hop on the treadmill for a four-minute walk while watching Oprah, and call these "Litvinovs."

To summarize: You may find this the fastest workout you've ever done. Don't be surprised if the workout seems too light or too easy at first. Judge the workout on the last set, not the first set.

Pick a lift you know. Hit eight good reps with it, and then sprint away for five seconds. Rest and repeat this two more times.

Next time you try the workout, try another lift and maybe go a bit longer on the sprint.

Do this easy progression about twice a week. If you choose to make this your whole leg workout, you've chosen wisely. If you're preparing for an athletic competition, try to see if this workout carries over to your field of play.

Don't measure rest periods the first few workouts. Let yourself recover fully. As the weights go up in the lift and the sprint gets around 10 to 20 seconds, try to zero in on three- to five-minute recoveries.

You'll need it.

Oh, one final note. Four years later, at the 1987 World Championships in Rome, John Powell—noticeably leaner, faster and more muscular—took second place in the discus. He was 40 years old (ancient in track and field), and this accomplishment is still considered one of the most amazing feats in track-and-field history.

Even Easier Strength

LET'S GET BACK TO the big question:

Is there an "easy" way to get strong?

Pavel Tsatsouline and I wrote about this in *Easy Strength,* and I carried on with this concept in *Intervention.*

Lift heavy.

Do the basic human movements.

Keep your reps and sets low.

Stop your sets and your workout before you get fatigued.

Don't even struggle.

Basically, never miss a rep; keep plenty in the tank, and keep coming back.

Each one of these points can be violated, and we can still make progress. Part of the fun of building an athletic career, and in life, is to tweak the rules a bit.

I *love* the notion of looking at a "given" and doing the opposite. But, before you choose to go contrarian, try to understand and at least appreciate the traditional way of weightlifting.

The history behind the history

In 1982, I received a master's degree in history. There has certainly been a lot of history since that day, but the discipline of the study of history has served me well in the interim. I remember one of the profs warning us that the word "research" is perfect.

"You will find something the very first time you begin a project. Then, you will lose it. It will take you months, maybe years to find it again. That's why we call it RE-search."

I laughed politely, left the classroom and found a few letters that would be the bulk of my thesis. Then, I couldn't find them again for nine months.

Not only was this true for my studies, but it is true in fitness and sports. My greatest insights have come when I discovered that what I learned in the first weeks of lifting and discus throwing continue to be the greatest lessons of my career.

My academic career didn't end in 1982; I went on to study religious education in depth for the next 30-plus years. There are lessons there, too. The threads that bind my approach to fitness, health and strength emerge as a tapestry that dates backward centuries and involves dozens of insights from others.

One of the basic lectures I give in my religious studies classes involves an important concept about community. Everyone seems to appreciate what I call the "horizontal community." As you already know, that would be the friends, family, church, group, team, society, brotherhood, sisterhood or whatever you belong to today. It can be as personal as blood relatives or simply bytes in an internet forum.

What most people miss is the "vertical community." Most often, the vertical community involves a story and, sadly, most of us forget ours. The vertical community are those people, those events and those tiny connections that knit together at some point and make the sublime of one generation seem obvious to another. To truly understand the concept of strength and conditioning, we need to go back a long ways.

We can all blame Milo, I guess. Milo was a wrestler and multi-time Olympic champion in the original Games. His good friend was Pythagoras, who made life easier with his idea that "The sum of the areas of the two squares on the legs (a and b) equals the area of the square on the hypotenuse (c)."

Milo also consumed, we are told, a daily amount of 30 pounds of meat, 20 pounds of bread and 18 pints of wine. But, that is not why we remember Milo. We remember him because of his idea to pick up a bull.

The story goes that, each day, he would walk out to the pasture and pick up a certain calf. The next day, he would repeat this until the bull was full grown. Milo is the father of progressive-resistance exercise, and it's his fault people think that success in strength training is a straight line. I have joked many times with new lifters that if you bench 100 pounds today and add only 10 pounds a week, about a year from now, you will bench more than 600 pounds. It sure works on paper.

Strongmen have had an interesting role in the development of Western Civilization. We certainly love to see a Beowulf show up when we have an issue with the various Grendels in our basements, but we also know that Little John will be spending more time at the buffet rather than sharpening his shooting skills like Robin Hood. Samson is going to kill a lot of Philistines, but his understanding of women is going to be dim at best.

A century ago, the concept of strongman and weightlifting had congealed into the saucy, mustachioed, leopard-print-wearing circus sideshow attraction. With the relatively small Harry Houdini breaking handcuffs, the strongman shows evolved into lifting members of the audience, being pulled or driven over by cars and carts, and the various one-arm lifts that seemed to dominate thought. But, how can you figure out who was truly the strongest?

With the reawakening of the Olympics in 1896, the "Olympic lifts" were contested. These would be unrecognizable by today's standards with the clean and press, which was eliminated in 1972 after having the longest tenure in the Games. The one-arm dumbbell lift, lowering the dumbbells, dumbbell curls, and one-arm press were all once part of the Games.

At the same time, George Hackenschmidt, a Russian wrestler and earlier proponent of strength training for sports and general health, began codifying the threads of lifting knowledge into a book called *The Way to Live*.

Hack's influence on the modern world of lifting comes to us in a strange direction. Down in the South Seas in Australia, a man named Percy Cerutty was changing his life of illness and weakness and adapting his new insights into coaching track-and-field athletes.

Cerutty asked Hack for advice, and the interactions between these two knitted together the links from the Old "Old School" to the modern approach of what I refer to as "Easy Strength." Hack outlined weight training into two parts: "extensive," which would be a volume (and hypertrophy) approach to training, and "intensive," a more load-focused (and, therefore, strength) method.

Cerutty adapted and adopted Hack's ideas. I once summed his work:

- ✦ Run up hills
- ✦ Lift weights

In addition, he insisted that all athletes do the big five lifts:

1. A deadlift

2. A form of pressing—Cerutty liked the bench press.

3. An explosive full-body move—He liked the heavy dumbbell swing.

4. A form of pulling—Cerutty liked pullups and cheat curls. Cheat curls are like a power clean with a curl grip (power curls) or that bouncing heavy-bar curl you see many trainees do.

5. An ab exercise—If deadlifts make you go one way, the ab exercise should strengthen you in the other.

After going heavy on these lifts with two to five sets of two to five reps—save for swings and abs where the reps go fairly high—you hang from a pullup bar and stretch for a few minutes.

At the same time Hack was corresponding with Cerutty, Drs. Thomas DeLorme and Arthur Watkins were working with both polio patients and soldiers injured in WWII. In 1945, DeLorme wrote a paper, *Restoration of muscle power by heavy-resistance exercises,* published in the *Journal of Bone and Joint Surgery.*

In 300 cases, he found "splendid response in muscle hypertrophy and power, together with symptomatic relief," by following this method of seven to ten sets of 10 reps per set for a total of 70 to 100 repetitions each workout. The weight would start off light for the first set and then get progressively heavier until a 10-rep max load was achieved. Over time, things changed in terms of volume. By 1948 and 1951, the authors noted:

> *"Further experience has shown this figure to be too high and that in most cases a total of 20 to 30 repetitions is far more satisfactory. Fewer repetitions permit exercise with heavier muscle loads, thereby yielding greater and more rapid muscle hypertrophy."*

A series of articles and books followed in which they recommended three sets of 10 reps using a progressively heavier weight in the following manner:

> *Set One—50% of 10-repetition maximum*
>
> *Set Two—75% of 10-repetition maximum*
>
> *Set Three—100% of 10-repetition maximum*

In this scheme, only the last set is performed to the limit. The first two sets can be considered warmups. In their 1951 book, *Progressive Resistance Exercise,* DeLorme and Watkins state:

> *"By advocating three sets of exercise of 10 repetitions per set, the likelihood that other combinations might be just as effective is not overlooked... Incredible as it may seem, many athletes have developed great power and yet have never employed more than five repetitions in a single exercise."*

I love that last line.

It's easy to miss their audience: injured vets and polio victims. My mother of Blessed Memory, Aileen Barbara McCloskey John, feared little in her life. She grew up very poor, and then things got worse with the Great Depression. Nearly every man in her life fought in various wars and, admittedly, I did see her cry every day when her sons were in Vietnam.

But, nothing frightened her except polio. Polio was the scourge of youth and destroyer of lives to generations. The causes were thought to be swimming pools, ice cream and open windows. And, literally overnight, with a series of vaccines, the curse ended. Modern weightlifting's ability to help victims of this disease regain the use of limbs allowed the barbell to become more mainstream in the eyes of many people.

While DeLorme and Watkins were rehabbing vets, Otis Chandler, a young Stanford shot putter and, later, the editor of the *Los Angeles Times,* began lifting weights to throw the shot farther. He did. He broke one of the longest-standing world records in history and drew a line in the sand: If you want to keep up in shot putting, you *have* to lift. Soon, to compete in any event in track-and-field, you had no option: You had to lift.

Yet, even 20-plus years later, when I first began to lift, I would hear two things:

"This stuff will make you muscle bound."

"This stuff will turn you homo."

Neither statement withstands the evidence of science or human dignity.

Yet, with polio victims regaining use of their limbs, it was obvious to many that to play in sport, you had to lift. Furthermore, the great Vladimir Janda, the physician and physical therapist, began his insights into tonic and phasic muscles and his various "crossed syndromes."

It is also important to note that he, too, was a victim of polio, that terrible disease of the last century. Janda's understanding that stretching—loosening—one muscle and strengthening its opposite would promote better structural integrity than attacking just one side of the equation.

One final thread: In Russia since the 1700s, local men had been testing their mettle against one another by lifting the traditional measure, the one- or two-pood—36 to 72 pounds—kettlebell against one another. This oddly shaped device stayed on the fringe of Russian and later Soviet sport through the modern age.

I remember the small black-and-white pictures of Soviet athletes tossing, tugging, jumping and juggling these odd cannonballs with handles. In the west, they were used alongside globe barbells until these basically disappeared with the advance of the standardized revolving barbell. I have magazines from the 1950s that remind readers not to ignore these important training items. Then, like Barbara Eden in *I Dream of Jeanie,* they vanished in a blink.

Until Pavel Tsatsouline emerged on the scene.

Pavel began his coaching in America in an abandoned bank safe. He offered inexpensive community-education programs and trained future Navy Special Operators with minimal equipment and lots of knowledge. After John Du Cane heard him speak, the two met later for coffee and began publishing books and making kettlebells for Americans.

Not long after, in 2004, Pavel was asked to speak at Charles Staley's bootcamp. Another speaker cancelled at late notice, and Charles scrambled to fill the one-hour hole. Mike Pockowski famously told Staley: "Dan John can fill an hour."

Who?

That next Saturday, I met Pavel, and he told me how to get stronger.

> *"For the next 40 workouts, pick five lifts. Do them every workout. Never miss a rep, in fact, never even get close*

to struggling. Go as light as you need to go, and don't go over 10 reps in a workout for any of the movements. It's going to seem easy. When the weights feel light, add more weight."

It was that simple. It was that easy. I followed the directions exactly and made the best strength gains of my life.

And, for whatever reason, few people have been able to follow those few simple sentences.

That was the beginning of "Easy Strength," which is the sum of the threads from Hack, Cerutty, DeLorme, Watkins, Janda and the Girevek kettlebell enthusiasts.

The reason it seems so contrarian today is another thread of the history of lifting: the bodybuilding and physique world. With Arnold and Jane Fonda pushing volume and the "burn" and rewarding those who want to spend time isolating every muscle, the classic methods of getting stronger with basic movements seemed to be laughable in its simplicity.

Success, honestly, is almost always the simple route. It might not be sexy to follow this approach; it might not have the gonzo, warrior, Spartan, or tactical title and tribal tats, but it works. It's hard to sell boring, but it works.

In my mind, the tradition of strength training supports the vision of reasonableness that I train in the "Easy Strength" fashion. What's hard to understand is this: It is a system, not just an interesting history lesson.

The basic basics

Chip Conrad has a very simple model for constructing a training program. At birth, your first physical-movement challenge was three-fold:

How to stand

How to sit

How to crawl

The key to understanding movement is seeing the flow between the three first challenges. If you master crawling and standing, you are certainly on your way to walking.

Many of the programs designed for people older than 30 skip this insight. That is why it is always wise to have the basic fundamental human movements in your training. Simply mixing a swing—a hinge—a goblet squat and a pushup in some kind of variation will bring you right back to your first years of life. If you mix and match things well, it will become dance-like in its flow. The devil, as always, is in the details.

Can you do more than this? Of course!

Can you use machines, ropes, bells of every sort and fashion, mats, rocks, anvils or tires?

Sure.

The answer to most "Can you?" questions in fitness is "Yes," clearly.

Can you lift light and get strong?

Now that's a good question. I experimented years ago with the idea of using light-to-moderate weights with very tight rest periods. For example, on big moves like the front squat or the overhead squat, I did three sets of eight repetitions with only a one-minute rest. The idea was to let the fatigue built up in the first two sets impact the third.

Did it work? Yes, in fact, I was staggered to find that this prepared me better for Olympic lifting meets than my standard idea of doing heavy front squats in sets of two or three.

But, I *never* missed a rep doing this program. My sets were low, and I remained fresh. My body liked the fact that I wasn't being crushed all the time and rewarded me with happy efforts on the lifting platform.

Should you move the barbell, for example, fast or slow? Should you do really high reps or low? The truth is this: *It all works.*

It always has, and it always will.

Years ago, I read Terry Todd's work explaining the need to vary reps over a few months. So…I did a month of 20 to 25 reps, a month of eight to twelve, and finished with a month of five to eight reps. In hindsight, I don't know why I didn't keep doing it, because I made excellent progress on my body composition. It didn't help me with my performance as much as singles and doubles, but one can easily see how these three months of following Todd's insights would be great for anyone.

In case you missed the point: It works because it all works.

How does it work?

Chip Conrad used the famous 30th episode of *South Park* to explain what happens. When the underpants gnomes are asked to explain their business plan, they pull out a chart that has this:

1. *Collect underpants*

2. *???*

3. *Make profit*

How does "this" work? If "this" is strength training, all we know is this:

To get stronger, lift weights.

Any and all clarity beyond this is suspect. The "???"—or my lack of understanding of how any of this works—is the fundamental principle of my coaching career.

Let us return to our basic point about my overarching principle: It's fine that we don't know how it works…if it works. Remember, we must follow the evidence, no matter where it leads.

> *"How often have I said to you that when you have eliminated the impossible, whatever remains, however improbable, must be the truth?"*
>
> ~ Sherlock Holmes, *The Sign of the Four*

For More from Dan John—

Wandering Weights: Our Epic Journey Through All Things Heavy

Sometimes you miss the most interesting training-related articles. Sometimes the ideas in the most talked-about articles are confusing. You're not sure what to think.

Sometimes Dan just makes you laugh.

We've gotcha covered! Each Wednesday, Dan gives us a short overview of what he's reading and what he's thinking about while he reads. All you have to do to get his free weekly review is to sign up.

And when you click the confirmation link, we'll send you a copy of Dan's five-page report on *The Quadrants of Diet and Exercise,* one of his most-discussed training concepts. Enter your email address at the link below to keep up with Dan's conversations.

http://danjohn.net/wandering-weights/

And you can also tap into the brains of some of the world's leading performance experts

You can also get free access to information from some of the world's leading performance experts through On Target Publications. You'll get the latest articles, interviews, specials and product-release details sent straight to your email.

You'll also get free lifetime access to the OTP Vault, which contains articles and videos from experts like Dan John, Gray Cook, Sue Falsone, Stuart McGill, Lorimer Moseley and others.

To get access to the OTP Vault, enter your name and email at the following link.

http://otpbooks.com/Dan-John-Book-Bonus

Secrets about the Author

IN AUGUST 1987, DAN JOHN was a high school history teacher who drove a rusted Volkswagen Super Beetle with its rear bumper held on by a weight belt. He had sworn off women and dating. He was convinced he would never get married or have kids.

All that changed one week before his 30th birthday. Dan agreed to accompany one of his assistant coaches to a party, where the coach was being set up on a date with a girl named Tiffini Hemingway. That began a whirlwind relationship resulting in a wedding in May of 1988. His fear of never being a father was alleviated in 1990 and again in 1992 with the birth of his daughters.

Dan's favorite holiday is Thanksgiving. He's such a fan that he insists on "practicing" Thanksgiving at least four times a year.

He received an Irish tin whistle as a gift and practices it every day.

Finally, the man is a crier. He tears up when he's happy, and he tears up when he's sad. Whether he's watching the opening scene of *Love Actually,* or attempting to get through singing a verse of *Danny Boy* to his grandson Danny, you had better make sure there are tissues nearby.

Two of Dan's favorite sayings are, "It's not where you start, it's where you finish" (the John family motto) and "Make a difference."

Dan John is proof positive of both.

Index